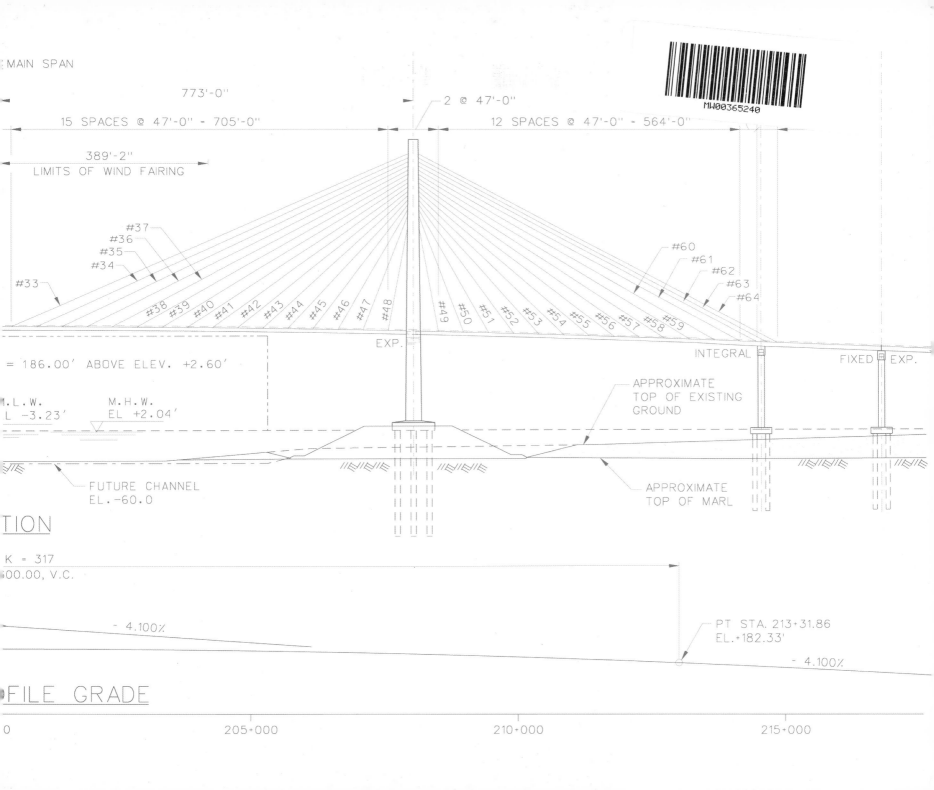

MAIN SPAN

773'-0"

2 @ 47'-0"

15 SPACES @ 47'-0" = 705'-0"

12 SPACES @ 47'-0" = 564'-0"

389'-2"
LIMITS OF WIND FAIRING

#33 #34 #35 #36 #37 #38 #39 #40 #41 #42 #43 #44 #45 #46 #47 #48 #49 #50 #51 #52 #53 #54 #55 #56 #57 #58 #59 #60 #61 #62 #63 #64

EXP.

INTEGRAL

FIXED EXP.

= 186.00' ABOVE ELEV. +2.60'

M.L.W.
EL -3.23'

M.H.W.
EL +2.04'

APPROXIMATE
TOP OF EXISTING
GROUND

FUTURE CHANNEL
EL.-60.0

APPROXIMATE
TOP OF MARL

TION

K = 317
500.00, V.C.

- 4.100%

PT STA. 213+31.86
EL.+182.33'

- 4.100%

FILE GRADE

205+000

210+000

215+000

6˝
9/1/5

The Bridge Builders

AND CHARLESTON'S GRAND NEW SPAN

The Bridge Builders

AND CHARLESTON'S GRAND NEW SPAN

TONY BARTELME & JESSICA VANEGEREN

EVENING POST PUBLISHING COMPANY
Charleston, South Carolina, USA

For additional information, please contact Evening Post
Publishing Company, 134 Columbus Street, Charleston,
South Carolina, 29403-4800, USA.   www.charleston.net

Book design by Gill Guerry
Editor: Doug Pardue

Printed and bound in The USA
by The R.L. Bryan Company

Library of Congress Cataloguing-in-Publication Data

Bartelme, Tony and VanEgeren, Jessica
    The Bridge Builders
    and Charleston's Grand New Span

ISBN 1-929647-08-5

SECOND EDITION
10 9 8 7 6 5 4 3 2 1

DEDICATED TO

Grace Kutkus, and all those who lost their lives on the old bridges

and

Miguel Angel Rojas Lucas, who died working on the new bridge

OPPOSITE:
A forest of cranes grows on the work site.

LEFT:
Joe Hill, ironworker, main span.

Introduction

The sun is the flint, flashing as it rises from the Atlantic, casting the first light on the spires of Charleston's new landmark. Shrimpers trawling outside the harbor can see what happens next: The sun turns the cables and towers pink, then yellow, and then the new Cooper River bridge suddenly looks like two diamonds in a spider web, or a double-masted sailboat. Sometimes there's fog, though, and you can't see the new bridge from the water or land. But the bridge builders are well into their day by now, and if they're on the towers, they might be above the fog, watching it as it curls around the peninsula of Charleston like big white arms. The bridge workers might notice the view, or they might not. They've seen it before. Besides, they're there to build a bridge, not gawk, and focus is required.

Bridge building remains a raw and risky endeavor. On average, a worker building a highway or bridge dies every four days, often from a fall. Despite advances in construction technology, bridge builders still grab huge steel beams with their hands and muscle them into place with pry bars. They work high over land and water, exposed to the weather. Their office is the space between points of land, an inherently unsafe place to spend time. For four years, more than 3,000 people called this bridge their office, and this book is about them.

Bridge builders rarely get any personal recognition for their work, and that's just fine for most. They can see what they've done from twenty miles away and tell their kids, "I tied the rebar on that bridge." But everyone knows they make something special. While skyscrapers and office buildings separate people, bridges connect us, and so bridges capture our imaginations like no other structure. Artists recognize the poetry of a bridge's form and function and like to paint pictures of them. Politicians know a good metaphor when they see one and slip bridges into speeches. Companies know it's good to link their businesses to something that belongs to everyone, so they put bridges on logos and signs. A bridge builder's creation has an unusual pull. It attracts the suicidal. People want to run over it just to say they did it. It changes the landscape forever, or until it's replaced by a new span.

A bridge usually has a history long before the first

OPPOSITE:
The John P. Grace Memorial Bridge, undated photo

builders arrive. To be sure, a bridge's origin can be as simple and serendipitous as a tree falling over a stream. More often it has to do with money.

That was the case with the John P. Grace Memorial Bridge, the first to link Charleston and its coastal suburbs to the north. In the late 1920s, owners of a resort on the Isle of Palms formed the Cooper River Bridge Corporation to build a toll bridge, and John P. Grace, a former mayor, pushed the project through. Fourteen people died during its construction, and when the first cars rolled over in 1929, the Grace was the fifth longest metal cantilever bridge in the world. With its narrow lanes and steep humps, it was dubbed "the first roller-coaster bridge," and it cost fifty cents to cross. It was no Golden Gate, but the Grace took its place, hanging like an old curtain of gray lace over the harbor.

The Silas N. Pearman bridge was built in the mid-1960s. Like the Grace, it was a metal cantilever bridge, but it lacked the Grace's delicate features. It had three lanes of traffic because the state didn't want to pay for four. When it opened, leaders already were predicting the need for a third bridge. In Charleston, the Pearman's on-ramp was a confusing gantlet of uphill merges. Over time, "the new bridge" became a symbol of short-sighted planning and mediocre engineering. It was like the tourist who moved to Charleston and then complained about the heat; it never quite fit in.

The origin of the new Cooper River bridge was the failure of these two old ones. Because the Grace was so narrow, it was a poor conduit for the area's growing traffic needs, and in the late 1940s, *The News and Courier* began writing stories and editorials calling for a new bridge, a campaign that would rise and fall like the tides rushing past the bridge's foundations. In 1957, the paper wrote that the bridge's ability to handle traffic "has been pitifully lacking." In 1979, the newspaper hired an engineer to study the Grace. When he was done, he vowed never to drive over it again. In 1985, state inspectors found cracked floor beams and a dangerous up-and-down movement when trucks rolled over the deck. In 1991, the highway department propped up part of the bridge with wooden beams.

Area leaders agreed that the Grace needed to go; the problem was the price tag. In the mid-1990s, officials estimated that a new one would cost at least $400 million. Sticker shock turned to gridlock. Local leaders were against tolls. The governor was against new gas taxes. Politicians in the Upstate considered it a Charleston project. Legislators in Charleston said it was a state responsibility. In 1995, area leaders formed what one called "the action committee." After several meetings, the committee disbanded.

But time has a way of gathering tinder. In the mid-1990s, the South Carolina State Ports Authority warned that a new class of container ships wouldn't fit under the old Grace and Pearman bridges, putting the port at a competitive disadvantage. H.B. "Buck" Limehouse, chairman of the state Highway Commission, began lobbying for a toll bridge and the creation of a special bank that would borrow money for large infrastructure projects. *The Post and Courier,* successor to the old *News and Courier* and *Evening Post,* focused on the issue with stories outlining what it would take to build the bridge and the failure of local leaders to take charge.

Then, a spark.

Arthur Ravenel Jr. remembers the day: February 24, 1995. He was in a crowded conference room at Mount Pleasant Town Hall when a highway department consultant issued a report on the Grace bridge. The consultant said that on a scale of one to a hundred, with a hundred being the highest score, the Grace rated a four. The crowd gasped. The score was based mainly on the Grace's narrow lanes, so the report was somewhat misleading; the bridge was in no danger of falling. But the number had power, and Ravenel had a cause. "That's the day I quit driving over that bridge," he recalled.

Soon after, Ravenel had lunch with his friend, Harry Hallman, a political mover and shaker from Mount Pleasant, who eventually would become mayor. Hallman urged Ravenel to run for the state Senate and make the bridge issue the centerpiece of his campaign.

Ravenel had been in politics for much of his adult life, first as a state legislator and later as a U.S. congressman. But in 1994, he ran for governor and lost, and he was eager to exercise his political muscles. With his name recognition and folksy ways, "Cousin Arthur," as he was called, easily won a senate seat. One of his first acts was to introduce legislation creating a bank for large infrastructure projects. The legislation passed, and over the next few years, Ravenel hounded the bank's leaders to make the bridge their top priority. He cajoled and sometimes bullied the ports authority and Charleston County into coughing up the equivalent of $150 million over the next twenty-five years as a local match. By 1999, the bridge project was under way. For Ravenel's efforts, the state Highway Commission and General Assembly named the bridge after him.

At more than $600 million, it was the largest single construction project in the state's history, and three large construction consortiums submitted bids. One group called itself Palmetto Bridge Constructors. It was led by Skanska, a large Swedish construction conglomerate, its American subsidiary, Tidewater Skanska Inc., and Flatiron Structures of Colorado. They promised to build an eight-lane cable-stayed bridge in less than four years, a year faster than the state required. That vow helped seal the deal.

And, in the summer of 2001, with the July sun turning Charleston's skies a blinding white, the bridge builders began to arrive.

Arthur Ravenel Jr.

The Bridge Builders

Chapter One

To Build a Bridge

They came from all over the world to work here, to build a stage in the sky, to build a grand bridge. They rolled in from Maine and Texas and Kentucky, towing campers behind their trucks.

They flew in from France and Sweden and Canada with blueprints and PowerPoints and a fondness for espresso.

They drove in from Moncks Corner and Santee and Goose Creek with new work gloves and steel-toed boots.

They came for the money, mainly, and the challenge, and when they weren't on the job, who knows? Maybe drink a few beers and chase a few women.

They came to dance with steel and concrete, to work in a place where men catch girders and beat on thick metal pins with sledgehammers.

While here, they would feel death's presence. Some would cheat it, watching it fall toward them like a nightmare monster, and be stopped at the last second by a net or an angel. Sometimes the monster came from the bridge deck or the cables, exploding like a jack in the box, grabbing anyone in reach.

To their surprise, in just four years, they built a living, breathing thing. Like a sunflower, the bridge moved twelve inches or more as the sun rose and warmed the young concrete. Then, as the sun set over the steeples of downtown Charleston, the towers moved back. Sometimes the workers, not God, moved the bridge. They used hydraulic jacks to bend the towers, and they tuned the long white cables like guitar strings to make the deck rise and fall.

They were proud of what they were making, but in ways only their families or bartenders would know. A job like this is never a clean or polite affair. The workers built this bridge with sweat, coffee, pranks, and more than a little yelling. They worked in rain so heavy they couldn't see past the tips of their hard hats, worked so long and hard they passed out in their chairs at home and woke the next morning in yesterday's clothes.

These moments would blind many of the workers to their achievement: Even before they connected the spans, their midair stage had become known throughout the

OPPOSITE:

Ironworker on approach ramp

world. People wanting to build bridges in other countries traveled here to see how these workers had done it - how they built a bridge a year ahead of schedule without losing money.

Success had its costs, though, and this job would consume as it created. A big construction job does that; companies bet fortunes and futures on projects like this, and the pressure falls from manager to worker like a mudslide, taking careers, marriages, and lives in its path. Because of this pressure, a big bridge job becomes a race — against time, weather, and the limits of human endurance.

And, now, on the windy morning of March 11, 2005, the race was all but over, and Dave Vannah was wondering where the hell his wife was. *She gets lost all the time,* he thought. He didn't want her to miss the big show.

Dave was a superintendent, a barrel-chested man with a curly mop of hair and a wide, windblown face. Today, his crew would drive in the Golden Spike, or rather, drop a ten-ton concrete slab into a gap on the road deck.

Once the gap was closed, the deck would be complete; the bridge would truly be a bridge. It would be a moment of great symbolism, and a convoy was on the way to witness it. The mayors of Charleston and Mount Pleasant were coming. So were the lawmakers and TV people in their suits and high heels.

And, as far as the workers were concerned, it was all for show. Hours earlier, when no one was watching, a crew lowered the last slab to make sure it fit and then lifted it back out. They didn't want any surprises in front of the cameras and bosses. They wanted to make it look easy, building this bridge, which it most certainly was not.

Many workers weren't sure whether to be amused or annoyed by the pomp. Tom Mitcham, a lanky foreman from Texas, milled about as the wind picked up. "If it starts raining, then they'd get a taste of what it's really like here."

Some were sad. For April Carder, this job had changed

her life, and now the work was ending. Others, such as Joseph Davis, were grateful to be part of history. José Lopes, a Frenchman, wasn't sure what was going on and busied himself on one of the cables.

As noon approached, Dave called his wife again. "Hurry up babe. I love you."

Then the convoy arrived, and the crowds gathered around the gap, and Wade Watson, the project manager, ordered Peo Halvarsson, the tall Swede, to lower the slab. Peo looked at Dave, who yelled, "Roll!"

The workers climbed around the slab.

"Carlos, you have five minutes to do this!" Dave yelled.

The crane rumbled.

"OK, guys, it's your time to shine."

ABOVE:
Joey Taiste inside a rebar cage

OPPOSITE:
Leon Daman, ironworker, main span

Chapter Two

The Lure of Bridges

March 1999

What next? Dave Vannah's 1987 Volvo began to lose power, as if a ghost was turning the key on and off. His wife, Susan, groaned. "This is a bad sign." Dave ran through the possibilities. *Must be the wiring.* They limped for twenty miles, toward a Volvo dealership in Baltimore. When they arrived, the parts man laughed: A new wiring harness? About $750 and two weeks to get here. Dave walked out, shaking his head. *We don't have time for this.*

Dave and Susan had packed everything they owned into the car so Dave could build a bridge in Myrtle Beach, a new concrete arch over the Intracoastal Waterway. It was a good job in a place much warmer than his hometown in Maine. He would be a foreman, and his supervisors had promised him a company truck. But he was running late now.

Dave looked around, spotted a store and dispatched Susan to buy rolls of black electrical tape. When she returned, they spent four hours rewrapping the wires in an empty parking lot. "God is telling us to go back," Susan said. But when he turned the key, the car fired up. Dave cheered; Susan burst into tears.

Dave hadn't bothered to call his bosses and tell them he would be late, so when he finally showed up at the job site, the supervisor told him his job had vanished. Bad thoughts flashed through Dave's mind. *You mean, I hit the road for nothing? What am I going to tell Susan?* Then salvation. The supervisor said he still had work for Dave, just not the foreman job he wanted. And, sorry, Dave, you'll have to wait for that company truck. Dave exhaled; penance was much better than unemployment.

● ● ●

Dave lived much of his life on the edge of a knife. That's the way it is with many bridge builders. They are risk takers. They work over places that are inherently dangerous: the sea, mountain gorges, busy highways. They're drawn to the rush of working high in the air, of making something larger than life.

OPPOSITE:

Dave Vannah, superintendent

As a boy on his father's farm in Maine, Dave built bridges and roads in his sandbox. Sometimes, playing wasn't so much about building things but taking stuff apart. When he was five, he dismantled an electric train he got for Christmas and then dissected his sister's talking doll. *Oh, so that's how it works.* As he grew older, he took apart cars instead of toys. After high school, he learned how lots of other things ticked. He worked as a house-mover, scallop-dragger, farmer, logger, and prison guard. He opened an auto body shop, but the business failed. He worked as a landscaper, iron-worker, carpenter, and he opened another body shop.

Then one day he saw a four-lane bridge going up in Bath, Maine, thirty minutes from his home. He was drawn to the structure and how it seemed to defy gravity. The tug-of-war began. *Should I apply? What about my auto shop? I'm thirty-eight. I'm too old. Changing jobs is too risky. What the hell, this would be interesting.*

He was hired as a laborer earning ten dollars an hour. At first, he stacked planks. Then, his boss gave him a chop saw and told him to cut rebar strands. When he was finished, he had chopped six miles worth. He plowed through his tasks like a big snow truck. Four weeks into the job, he figured out how to remove jacks that had frozen to the bridge. He took an hour; the other welders had taken the whole day. The welders told him:

"Slow down."

"Relax."

"You're working too fast."

But Big Dave was a bridge builder now. And bridge builders don't have the luxury of wasting time. Motorists want faster traffic; politicians want to please taxpayers; companies want the job done quickly so they can bid on more jobs. Dave made games out the grunt work, trying to finish tasks as fast as he could. *If I get this out of the way, they'll give me something better.* After three months, he was running a crew, and people started calling him "Mr. Bridge" because he loved his job so much.

He had started on the Bath, Maine, bridge two days after marrying Susan. They had met years before at summer camp. She was an awkward twelve-year-old camper then; he was a husky fifteen-year-old hired to pick up trash and do odd jobs. One night, they broke away from the campers and sat with their feet dangling from a dock, watching moonbeams dance on the camp's lake. Susan was smitten, but Dave had his eye on a nineteen-year-old counselor. He even asked the older girl out to a Bob Dylan concert, their first and last date.

Some twenty years later, Susan drove into Dave's body shop with a friend, and the memory of that moonlit night on the lake flooded back. Soon, they were at parties together, talking all the time, hanging on each other's words, whirling like electrons around a nucleus. Dave couldn't take his eyes off this petite, spunky woman with curls longer and darker than his. They were both outgoing; they each had been married before, Dave twice, Susan once; they both had two children from previous marriages. Dave told everyone that Susan was his soul mate, his queen. They had way too much chemistry not to get married. Six months later, they said their vows. Dave felt his personal life was finally on track. He left his "Just Married" sign on

Crew works on rebar for downtown ramp

his car for a month.

Still, the move from Maine to Myrtle Beach was tough on Susan. She missed her two teenage children, who stayed in Maine, and Dave was always so busy with his job. She was left alone and felt little connection to Myrtle Beach. They had fun going to the mountains and stock car races on the weekends, but she missed Maine's rocky coast.

Then, with just three months left to go in Myrtle Beach, Dave heard about a big bridge going up in Charleston.

It would be the largest cable-stayed bridge in North America, a new landmark in a city famous for its old landmarks. *That's where I want to go next.* He told his crew, half-joking: "I'm going down to build one of those towers." They laughed. There goes Dave again, building bridges in his head.

But Dave liked his chances on this one. His company, Flatiron Structures Inc., was part of Palmetto Bridge Constructors, a consortium that had won the job.

He drove to Charleston to meet Wade Watson, the project manager.

Dave told him he was a working supervisor, a boss who gets his hands dirty. "If you're not interested in someone like that, I'm not your man." Watson liked that. He was the same way.

The two hopped in Watson's truck and drove across the old Cooper River bridge. Watson quickly sketched out what needed to be done.

The bridge would be three and a half miles long from end to end. It would require two diamond-shaped towers. They would be 573-feet tall. Between the towers, a metal and concrete deck would stretch 1,546 feet, allowing the world's biggest ships to pass through. Cables would be strung from the towers to support the deck, eight lanes wide plus a sidewalk for pedestrians. It wouldn't be easy.

Dave turned to Watson. "I want to build one of those towers — from start to finish."

RIGHT:
Crew boats and
the towers at sunrise

The Bridge Builders

OPPOSITE:
Just after sunup, workers
take boats to the rock islands.

LEFT:
Welder Corey Rollins and
other workers inside
east tower

13

Chapter Three

Human Chemistry

Summer 2001

Wade Watson often looked like a man in a hurry. He talked as fast as an auctioneer, his thick mustache wiggling to keep up. When he said "Ten-Four" on his two-way radio, it came out like a quick cough. He was fidgety with pens. He made decisions fast, and he rode his Harley fast to relieve stress. This was the biggest job in his life, and it was going to run like one of his bikes: fast and loud.

A few days after Palmetto Bridge Constructors inked its deal to build the new Cooper River bridge, Watson walked into the project's first office, a vacant brick building in a dilapidated neighborhood off Morrison Drive. A group of designers and engineers tagged along. "We gotta hit the ground running," he said. "We gotta get moving." He drew up a to-do list. It was ten pages long.

He phoned steel fabricators and other suppliers to get them up to speed. He recruited a veteran equipment manager, Henry Wood, to scour South Carolina and the rest of the nation for cranes and trucks. Watson was partial to South Carolina; he grew up in Cheraw, a little town near the North Carolina border, and had an engineering degree from Clemson University. He told Wood to pump as much money into South Carolina as he could.

The president of Tidewater Skanska had warned Wood and Watson: "I'm going to give you $25 million, but spend it wisely." The list of suppliers ballooned. Georgetown Steel would manufacture the cables; Wando Concrete would supply the concrete. Wood ordered tug boats, crew boats, forty-two cranes of all sizes, forty welding machines, and more than one hundred passenger trucks. He ordered a Rotec, a giant concrete hopper, and Putzmeisters, trucks capable of pumping five thousand pounds of concrete every minute.

Within a month, a trailer complex grew in a mud patch off Morrison Drive. Designers poured in with their laptops, blueprints and ideas. This was the big push now: design, design, design. Watson could hear the clock ticking. Their contract gave them five years to build the bridge. Miss that

deadline, and they would fork over $30,000 for every day they were late.

To make their deadline, they would design and build at the same time, a risky plan. A mistake early on could generate months of extra work down the road. In construction, delays spread like cancer. They mutate into public relations problems that lure lawyers and television people and cause more delays. Nothing like that had happened on any of Watson's other projects, but he had never built a cable-stayed bridge before, either.

The cable-stayed bridge is the suspension bridge's younger brother. On a suspension bridge, two massive cables stretch from an anchorage on one side of a river to an anchorage on the other. Two towers hold up the cables, like giants with ropes on their shoulders. Hanging from these master cables are smaller cables called "suspenders" that hold up the road deck. Suspension bridges can span wider distances than cable-stayed bridges, but suspension bridges have more parts and are more expensive to build.

On a cable-stayed bridge, cables are strung directly from the towers to the deck, making an A-shaped harp. The towers alone support the load, so no anchorages are needed. Cable-stayed bridges go up quickly and require less steel than suspension bridges. The Alex Fraser Bridge in Vancouver, Canada, was built in just twenty-seven months. With a span of 1,526, it was the longest cable-stayed bridge in the world when it opened in 1986, a title it kept until the early 1990s when longer bridges were built in Asia. (The Tatara Bridge in Japan is the current record-holder with a span of 2,919 feet.)

The new bridge over the Cooper would have a 1,546-foot span, a tad more than the Alex Fraser Bridge and more than 200 feet longer than the Dames Point Bridge in Jacksonville, Florida. However, the biggest engineering

challenge facing Watson and his designers had little to do with the bridge's length or the height of its towers.

The state wanted the bridge to survive a Category Five hurricane, one more powerful than Hugo, and an earthquake measuring 7.3 on the Richter Scale, as devastating as the one in 1886 that leveled much of the city. For an engineer, this dual requirement was a tough assignment.

In theory, a hurricane-proof bridge should be rigid, while an earthquake-proof bridge should be flexible. This bridge had to be both. Out came the wind tunnels and the calculations from the computer models and the gray hairs, and while engineers were at it, they had to design fifteen access ramps and figure out how the bridge could withstand a collision from a ship the size of an aircraft carrier. Tick, tick, tick.

ABOVE:

Jose Valdez and Gerard Middleton work on rebar column

OPPOSITE:

Tower crane's lights pierce the night fog

In came the Swedes. Lars Landen was one of the first to arrive, a short, boyish engineer who had just finished working on the Oresund Bridge, a 1,600-foot cable-stayed span linking Sweden and Denmark, slightly larger than the one in Charleston. Watson put Landen in charge of the main span: the towers and the cables. Another Swedish engineer, Peo Halvarsson, arrived soon after. Halvarsson was so tall that he barely cleared a standard six-foot-eight door frame when he wore a hard hat and boots.

The Swedes began working with architects and designers with Parsons Brinckerhoff, a company founded by the chief engineer of the New York subway. Because of the

bridge's complexity, the state of South Carolina hired a team led by T.Y. Lin International of San Francisco and HDR of Omaha, Nebraska, to monitor the work.

Building this bridge would be a massive experiment in human chemistry, and Watson knew each element in this concoction would be put under intense pressure. So he was grateful when he heard Bobby Clair Jr. talk about "partnering."

Clair sat atop the project's leadership pyramid. His official title was director of engineering and special projects for the South Carolina Department of Transportation. But the bridge was his sole responsibility. In an unusual move, the state gave him authority to make important decisions without going through the department's normal bureaucratic channels. This would speed the construction process, it was hoped, but it also put tremendous pressure on Clair.

He set the tone during the project's kickoff meeting, which was held in a conference center at Middleton Place plantation. More than forty people crowded the room, many speaking with European accents. Clair stood up and told them he was from Charleston, that his grandfather helped build the Grace bridge, and that he would make darn sure the state got its money's worth. Today would be the first partnering meeting, he told them, and they would have many others. These meetings would be held away from the work site so everyone could focus. If anyone thought this was too much communication, they should find another bridge to work on.

The next morning, Clair made sure the Swedes were served plates of instant grits at breakfast. It was a Southern delicacy, they were told. The Swedes were polite and said the grits were delicious. Clair and other locals laughed, finally telling them that instant grits are nothing special, no matter what country you're from. The Swedes had been initiated.

The momentum grew quickly, and the designers swigged coffee and built a bridge in their computers. They had digital hurricanes and ships smash into their virtual towers. They shook their bridge with earthquakes, making the deck bounce up and down like a toddler shaking a sheet. Their computers transformed calculations into girder lengths and concrete slabs.

Mike Abrahams ran the design team for Parsons Brinckerhoff, splitting time between his office in New York and Charleston. Like many bridge builders, he had a soft spot for big machines and buildings. When he was four, he spent hour after hour watching a construction project across the street from his house. On one rainy day, his

mother called him to come inside, but he wouldn't budge. A dump-truck driver saw the standoff and volunteered to give the boy a ride. His mother agreed, and Mike Abraham's future in construction was sealed.

He would help design many bridges during his career, though the one over the Cooper River would be the first in a place prone to both hurricanes and earthquakes. Some aspects of the design were givens: The towers would be shaped like diamonds; that had been decided in public hearings. Also, to make sure two large container ships would have room to pass each other, the bridge would have to cross the river's 1,000-foot-wide shipping channel. But thousands of other details had yet to be

Bobby Clair Jr., project director for South Carolina Department of Transportation

RIGHT:
Workers guide concrete
hopper to new pier

OPPOSITE:
Curt Stewart, paving
machine operator,
on approach ramp

worked out, and when the team's engineers tweaked the locations for the towers, they realized the span would be 1,546 feet, a record in North America. No one had asked them to set a record; it was just a pleasant surprise.

His team grew a hundred strong, even though many aspects of the bridge weren't particularly original. Engineers began with plans modeled on the Alex Fraser Bridge, working closely with that bridge's architects, Buckland & Taylor of Vancouver. The design of the Charleston bridge also resembled the Seohae Grand Bridge over South Korea's Asan Bay, and the approach spans were similar to Bangladesh's Paksey Bridge.

As Mike Abrahams and his team worked on design issues, Wade Watson and other managers focused on how to put this big puzzle together.

Some thought the bridge should be built in steps — towers first, then the deck and cables. That would be more orderly than building the deck and towers at the same time. It would require fewer calculations, which meant fewer chances to make mistakes that might cause the bridge to line up wrong.

But the Swedes thought otherwise: They had just done two cable-stayed bridges and had hung the cables while the bridge towers were still going up. Do the same thing on this bridge, and they might save three or four months, they said.

They hashed out this and other issues during partnering meetings at the Sand Dunes Club, an old reception hall owned by SCANA on Sullivan's Island. With the Atlantic Ocean crashing beyond the dunes, the designers, managers, and state engineers eventually agreed with the Swedes, then washed down oysters with beer to calm their nerves.

Chapter Four
The Locals

January 2002

Bink's phone rang one cold morning.

"You ready to work?" It was a foreman from Palmetto Bridge Constructors.

"I sure am," he said.

"Be there at 7 a.m."

Greg Binkley was a welder with a gruff voice that sounded like a small pickup truck going uphill. He was fifty and had an easy smile and long gray hair that he usually wore in a ponytail. Most of his body was covered with tattoos. He had done them himself in Ohio, where tattoos were legal. He moved to South Carolina fifteen years ago because it was warmer here, and the employment picture was brighter. Most everyone, even his wife, called him Bink, which conveniently rhymed with ink. His business card during his tattooing days said "Ink by Bink."

Bink had been calling the Palmetto Bridge Constructors hiring office for weeks, asking about openings. He had worked at Detyens Shipyard at the old Charleston naval base for several years. But he was ready for a change, and he liked the idea of building something that would outlast him. He thought, *My kids' kids will drive over that bridge and say, "my granddaddy built that."*

The next morning, he drove from his home near Summerville to the bridge employment office, a former auto repair shop on Meeting Street in downtown Charleston. A few protesters picketed outside, complaining that Palmetto Bridge Constructors hadn't hired enough local workers and wasn't paying union-scale wages. Bink slipped quietly through the doors. A protester followed and asked where he was from.

"Summerville," Bink replied.

"Looks like they got one local," the picketer snarled, as Bink thought, *Looks like I'm shooting their theory all to hell.* The next day, Bink started welding rebar on an iron cage, making fourteen dollars an hour plus time and a half for overtime work.

Bink's wife, Diane, was glad and a little relieved when she learned her husband would be working on the bridge.

OPPOSITE:

Derrick Clinton smoothing concrete on approach ramp

Her grandfather had helped build the John P. Grace Memorial Bridge. It was nice to have this generational link. More important, the job offered medical benefits, which was comforting because she was having health problems. Still, the hours were brutal. Bink was up at 4:30 a.m. and often stayed until late at night, six days a week. He called her without fail at lunch, and he knew she was worried that he might fall asleep when he drove home, so he called her again at quitting time.

• • •

Over the next few months, Bink and several hundred workers built steel rebar cages for the bridge's pilings. They built platforms into the marsh, and the bridge ramps began to grow like vines from each side of the river. Workers barged in 1.6 million tons of stone from Canada and dumped them in two rectangular piles just outside the shipping channel. Now the harbor had two new islands, one for the east tower, and one for the west. The rock was there to protect the towers if a ship veered out of control. Next, workers planted the rebar cages 230 feet into the clay below the Cooper River, deep enough to keep the ramps and towers steady in an earthquake.

Like these deep shafts, many workers had strong Low-country roots. Joseph Davis stood out, partly because he was sixty-two and one of the older workers out there, but mainly because he was a dignified man who didn't curse like the others. People called him "Mr. Joe" because simply calling him Joe didn't seem right. He was from Moncks Corner and had a wide, toothy smile. He had been in construction for more than thirty years, choosing jobs that were close to home because he didn't want to be away from his children. Over the years, he had seen many people get hurt on the job, and a few die. While working on the new bridge over the Wando River, he watched a speed loader run over a friend. Another worker there fell

OPPOSITE:
Greg "Bink" Binkley, welder

LEFT:
Scaffolding for the towers

thirty feet and died. Mr. Joe rarely got hurt, though. Sure, he chopped off a piece of his left ring finger one time, and another time when he was cutting metal, some hot shavings flew down his pants. But like many experienced workers, Mr. Joe had a sixth sense about which areas on a construction site were dangerous, and which places were safe. And, he was quick to chide younger workers who took chances, though not in a mean way. "Hey, you're jeopardizing yourself and your family," he said one morning to a worker without a safety harness. "You can make ninety-nine steps, but the one you miss is the one that can kill you."

Mr. Joe had the aura of a clergyman, so workers sometimes sought him out for advice. One afternoon a young worker asked him about women. "Stay away from the negative women," Mr. Joe said. "You don't buy a bucket with a hole in it, do you?" Mr. Joe was quick to tell people how hard work pays off, quick to talk about how he put four of his five children through college on a working-man's pay, quick to say how wonderful it was to watch the sunrise and sunsets from the water, quick to praise God for having the health and strength to do the kind of work many young men found too difficult.

Sometimes, he talked with Terry Brown, a laborer who grew up in Red Top, a tiny community in the marshland west of Charleston. Terry was thirty, tough as a linebacker, and thinking about quitting construction and getting into the insurance business. Mr. Joe urged him to follow his dream. Stay focused. Stay positive.

Mr. Joe began working on the tower cages, the bridge's skeleton, preparing them for the concrete, the towers' muscle and skin. One of his jobs was to insert long strands of rebar and tie it to other pieces, a job known as "rod busting." He went through pair after pair of work gloves, and sometimes when he got home, his whole

body ached. But Mr. Joe didn't dwell on these things. Instead, as the towers grew, and the view of the harbor and city opened up, he thought, *You never know how beautiful a place is until you get above it.*

● ● ●

For David Hand, the new bridge could make or break his business. Hand was a co-owner of Wando Concrete, which won a contract to supply 320,000 cubic yards of concrete, enough to create a solid block the size of a sports coliseum. His company was one of the smallest concrete suppliers in the area, but now he was working on the biggest project in the state's history. Stress levels were high.

First, he and his crews had to figure out the logistics of making and moving so much concrete. The sand would come from pits off South Carolina Highway 61, near the Black River, and the fly ash from power plants across the state. The rock was being mined from a quarry in Columbia, South Carolina. Finally, the cement would come from Greece and arrive in the bellies of fifteen freighters. Everything would then be mixed in a plant on Charleston's peninsula. From there, the concrete would be poured into trucks and taken to a loading operation at the foot of the Grace bridge. Workers would transfer the concrete to big gray hoppers and barge it to the islands, where it would finally be dumped into concrete molds. That was the easy part.

Hand and his workers also had to make concrete strong enough to withstand 7,000 to 8,000 pounds of pressure per square inch. This was more than twice as strong as standard concrete, and exponentially more difficult to make. They also had to make sure this ultra-strong concrete hardened in less than twenty-four hours, so workers could pour another section the next day. A typical concrete pour took twenty-eight days to reach its maximum strength. As far as Hand knew, no one had tried to harden high-strength concrete so quickly.

Hand and his mixing team began working with engineers from Palmetto Bridge Constructors to figure out the logistics and correct chemistry. He was grateful for the collaboration. Lots of companies would have simply ordered the concrete, and then hammered them if they didn't perform. *They could beat a little company like ours to death if they wanted,* Hand thought. But they worked together making test batches, forming samples into concrete cylinders, and then smashing them at Palmetto Bridge Constructors' lab to measure their strength.

On the day of the first pour for the tower base, Hand watched anxiously as the gray globs slithered into the forms. *It's out of our hands now,* he thought. He stayed up the whole night, working on other pours. He was so nervous, he wouldn't have been able to sleep anyway. The next morning, he went to Palmetto Bridge Constructors' lab off Meeting Street to watch them test the concrete from the tower. They took a cylinder and set the machine to break it. At the proper strength level, the concrete cracked. Everyone slapped each other on the back. It was about ten in the morning, but Hand and the others went out for beers.

●　　●　　●

The job site began to grow larger every day as workers drilled more and more shafts for the approaches, nearly 400 in all. Scattered across the job site were crews of Hispanics, some legal, some not. They spoke minimal English and were clumped together with bilingual supervisors.

Miguel Angel Rojas Lucas was on one such crew. He was twenty years old and had a round, slightly pudgy face. He and his two brothers and brother-in-law worked

Greg "Bink" Binkley

for Anatek, an Atlanta subcontractor, working on the Charleston interchange, a task that took him seventy-five feet above Town Creek.

Miguel is the happy one, his mother often thought. She had traveled to North Charleston five years before to find work and was now cleaning rooms in a local hotel. She had left Miguel and his two brothers and two sisters behind in Mexico, but over the years, they had also made their ways north. Miguel was now living in a small apartment next to her. She made lunch for him before he left for work, and they often shared coffee. When he wasn't working, he spent hours at the local arcade with his brothers. Miguel had taken several construction jobs before getting hired to work on the bridge, and he often told his mother it was the most difficult job he had ever had. But

he happily strapped on his tool belt and cut metal panels that would form the bottom layer of road deck.

● ● ●

For a while, most of Bink's crew barely spoke English, which was fine with him. He thought the Hispanics worked harder than many Americans, and working on rebar didn't require much talking anyway.

One spring morning, federal agents set up a checkpoint and detained thirty-one Hispanic workers from Mexico and Honduras. The men said they were working on the bridge, or laying railroad ties for a crane. Most were deported. Bink noticed that when U.S. Border Patrol agents rolled in, many Hispanics on his crew would vanish. Bink figured they were the illegal ones, though one time a Swedish supervisor made himself scarce because he didn't have his papers on him.

A few months after Bink was hired, he was sent to Drum Island to weld rebar for the approaches. He called it "the penal colony." It was a dirty and isolated place full of mud dredged from the harbor. On hot days, the muck held in the heat, and the dirty plastic portable toilets seemed to be the last ones on the job site to be cleaned. Bugs flew in clouds, and every once in a while, the county mosquito sprayer would douse them with pesticide. Workers would yell at the sky and shake their fists.

One day, Bink and a supervisor took a boat from Drum Island to the tower islands to see how the cages were being put together. He bumped into Dave Vannah, who seemed to be barking at everyone on his crew. *There's one of those hurry-up guys that can get you killed*, Bink thought.

Bink eventually was made a foreman, the equivalent of a sergeant in the Army. He didn't see it as a promotion. Foremen get hit from all sides — by workers who don't want to work and bosses who don't think your guys are working fast enough. And in any crew, there's always a jackass. One time, he confronted a worker about coming to work late. The worker got in his face, and Bink's hands curled into fists. He thought about hitting the guy but mouthed a kiss instead. The worker backed off, confused, and Bink uncurled his fingers.

As Christmas neared in 2003, Bink climbed up a rebar cage seven feet or so without attaching a safety cord. He knew he should have tied off, but he thought he could save a few minutes without a line. But the company had a rule: If you climb more than six feet off the ground and don't tie off, you're out. Supervisors wore stickers on their hard hats that said "Tie or Die." A safety guy happened to see Bink climb the cage and fired him on the spot.

Diane was wrapping presents when Bink came home. "I lost my job," he said. Diane didn't know what to say.

"It'll be all right," Bink said. He always said that, and that usually was enough for her. But his daughter overheard what had happened from her room and lectured him for half an hour. Bink let it wash over him. He felt bad. She was thirteen and had enough chaos in her life just being thirteen, and sometimes you have to let people blow off steam.

Besides, he wasn't too worried about his job prospects; a welder usually can find work. But he found that companies weren't interested in hiring people right before Christmas, and the bills began to pile up. Diane went to the food bank.

"It'll be all right," Bink said.

After the New Year, Bink reapplied for his job on the bridge. Soon after, he got another phone call. You're coming back to work, the foreman said. And there was more good news: He wouldn't be working on Drum Island anymore; they needed him on the towers, which were growing taller by the day.

OPPOSITE:

A night-shift worker on an approach ramp

Net catches debris in tower accident

30

Chapter Five

Fear and Danger

January 2004

Crreak, creeak, creeaak.

On the east tower, 300 feet above the Cooper River, 8,000 pounds of plywood and steel formwork started to sway.

Mark Sisney was on a platform attached to the formwork and felt it move and groan. *What the* … He scrambled to another part of the platform. Then, with a crack, the place where he had just been standing vanished.

April Carder looked up from a barge below. She heard the sounds above, and then it started to hail wood and steel; she saw a huge mass spiraling toward the bridge deck.

Lewis Williamson, Slim Mitcham and several other ironworkers were in the middle of the hailstorm, about to erect a girder on the bridge deck. One board hit a worker on his foot as he scrambled for shelter. Mitcham ducked into a small concrete doorway in the tower, grabbing another worker by his left shoulder.

April screamed into her walkie-talkie, "Is everybody OK? Is everybody OK?" Joe? Mike? Carlos? Mark? Why isn't anybody answering? She had a dark thought: *Were bodies mixed in with the debris?*

Then, a miracle.

A nylon net strung between the tower legs caught the bulk of the formwork. The net was designed to catch 350 pounds of debris, or maybe a bridge worker or two, not four tons. Somehow it held.

Underneath the towers, April couldn't see the net catch the formwork. She tried to keep her composure. She had been hired four months before, and she had fought hard to gain the respect of the guys. *You don't cry on a construction site, right?* But her boyfriend, Joe Rush, was up there, *and why can't I get any answers?*

Thirty minutes later, when Joe and the other workers came down, some were in tears. One said he had a pregnant wife at home; he didn't need this. Their hands were shaking from the adrenaline. Supervisor Dave Vannah wanted the crews to start cleaning up, but Slim Mitcham

April Carder and her son make pizza

and the others would have none of that. After talking with the safety people, they went straight to a bar.

The accident was the worst so far in the project, which, until then, had had remarkably few. Afterward, a handful of workers quit. Two were fired, including the foreman who had rigged the formwork. April thought about quitting, but this job had changed her life.

● ● ●

For the first time since April had left Florida and a failed marriage, she was making decent money. She had moved to Charleston five years earlier, a single mom with two boys. She had lived paycheck to paycheck, working for small construction companies around the Charleston area.

She moved sixty miles away to a tiny, white wooden house in Santee because she couldn't afford housing in the city. Now, she was making a good $1,100 a week with overtime. Money aside, she had proven something to herself on this job.

When she started, she was terrified of heights. She told Dave Vannah she would work only on the rock islands at the base of the towers. Dave knew she was scared, but told her if she wanted a job, she would have to climb.

April was the only woman on the towers. Stout with chin-length blond hair and pale blue eyes, she wore a small, silver rectangular-shaped nose ring that she sometimes swapped with a circular hoop. Four silver charms dangled around her neck, a sun, heart and two moons, presents from her two boys, including her eighteen-year-old, who had moved back to Florida. Take away the construction hat, safety glasses, work pants and boots, and she looked younger than her thirty-seven years.

She had started on the night shift. She only got four to six hours of sleep each night, but it wasn't as bad as she thought. She made it back home in time to make breakfast for her fourteen-year-old son before he left for school.

It was the guys on the bridge that took some getting used to. They could be rude, crude, and pushy, especially when they smelled weakness.

They knew April was afraid of heights. One night, a supervisor high on the east tower radioed that he needed a screwdriver. The workers made sure she was the one to take it to him. She steeled herself and climbed 180 feet up the scaffolding.

Then came the next phase of her initiation — the pranks. The guys made her search for "gator-tail saws." She quickly learned that "plum-bob oil" doesn't exist either. One day she found herself trapped in a portable toilet. Joe Rush had wired the door handle shut. As the workers laughed, she kicked her way out. Later, when Joe ducked in, she locked him in. She was learning.

Joe had encouraged her to apply for a job, and after the platform collapsed, he urged her to stay. "Don't let the fear get to you," he said.

It took April a week to persuade herself to stay. The fear lingered for months, like a slow-healing wound. She noticed everyone seemed more cautious every time another section of the formwork was lifted above their heads. For a while, Dave Vannah didn't entirely trust his crew. Without that net, his guys could have been wiped out. He asked more questions than he needed to. "What are you doing, April?" and "Make sure you're safe, Mark."

● ● ●

On a blistering day in May, there was another accident. It was noon, and Miguel Angel Rojas Lucas was working on the approach ramp from Charleston. He and the others broke for lunch. As Miguel walked toward his brother and brother-in-law, he slipped between some planks.

"Our brother has fallen into the water!" one of Miguel's brothers screamed. "Miguel has fallen!"

Crane operator David Gordon was eating lunch on a barge on Town Creek, seventy-five feet below, when he heard a splash. David thought the crew above had dropped something until he heard the shouting from the workers. Then he saw Miguel's hands break the surface.

David grabbed a life preserver and jumped into the water. But Miguel was wearing a tool belt, and he couldn't swim. He disappeared beneath the surface before David could get to him and as Miguel's brothers watched from above. Miguel's body was found three days later.

April and the other workers on the towers didn't know Miguel, but the death was still a jolt, a reminder that you had to stay alert.

The accidents brought the crew on the east tower to-

gether. They worked harder and were more focused, and they began to catch up to the crews on the west, the tower closest to Charleston. They topped off the east tower May 22, 2004, just eight days after workers on the west finished, the construction equivalent of a photo finish.

By then, April's fear of heights was gone, and sometimes when she went up in a manbasket, a metal cage dangling from the tower crane, she looked down at the river 600 feet below and across the harbor and felt like she was flying.

The race to build the towers was over, but a big bridge job has many races, even races within races. Now, a new race would begin, with new competitors and hurdles, a race in the air that would end only when the two road decks met in the middle.

TOP:
Rescue workers search for Miguel Angel Rojas Lucas

ABOVE:
Miguel Lucas

RIGHT:
Ironworkers on an
approach ramp

OPPOSITE:
Fernando Mariano
and David Reyes dangle
in manbasket, east tower

34

36

Chapter Six

The Ironworkers

December 2004

Danny Fields was 200 feet in the air, stepping slowly on a metal beam, his eyes focused on a 960-pound clamp a few feet ahead of him.

Fields and other ironworkers on the Cooper River bridge project had spent the day building this metal stage. They had hoisted steel from a barge, muscled the beams into position, and pounded pins with twelve-pound sledgehammers. Then they popped bolts into the bolt-holes to connect the beams and tightened nuts with an impact wrench that sounded like a machine gun.

Now Danny and another ironworker, Leon Daman, had to walk out onto this metal skeleton and release two huge clamps that had held the section in place.

Danny slipped his feet a few inches at a time, slowly, like an old man wearing slippers. The beam was 125-feet long and two feet wide, a virtual patio for ironworkers like Danny. But this beam had a foot-wide row of metal studs sticking up in the middle, leaving just a few inches of real

estate for his feet. Because of these studs, he and the other ironworkers tucked their pant legs into their boots. If he did trip, he had no handrails to grab, just air.

But he liked working up here in the sky, one wrong step from the void. The weather was different; on the ground, a light breeze often greeted workers as they boarded the crew boats. But up on the road deck, it might be blowing fifteen miles per hour or more. And higher, on top of the towers, it could be even colder and windier, and with the view, you felt as if you were flying in an open-cockpit airplane.

Like other ironworkers, that's where Danny felt at home. And he seemed built for this work, with short stocky legs that gave him a lower center of gravity and better balance.

Danny was a Lumbee Indian from Lumberton, North Carolina, and his nickname on the job was, predictably, "Lumbee." He had a half-inch scar on his forehead from a high-school knife fight. One of his ancestors was Henry Berry Lowry, who went underground during the Civil War

**Danny "Lumbee" Fields,
ironworker, west tower**

when the Home Guard killed his father and brother. Lowry raided plantations, often having dinner with his victims first, and had a $12,000 bounty on his head, a fortune in those days. He was never caught. Ironworkers like to think of themselves as outlaws, and Danny was proud of his heritage. He was friendly and focused, and his bosses liked him because he worked fast and hard.

Step, step, step.

Danny waddled toward the center of the beam. Leon was already there, holding onto his clamp. He bounced up and down ever so slightly, jiggling the girder to make Danny's space walk more interesting. It was a game iron-

workers liked to play.

Trailing behind Danny was a thick cord known as a yo-yo. It was connected to a girder and was supposed to jerk tight if Danny fell. In a fall, a 185-pound man like Danny might put more than 3,000 pounds of pressure on the line, not enough to snap it but certainly enough to snap something inside Danny.

Twenty-five feet, thirty feet, thirty-five feet.

Danny's yo-yo stretched out. A few inches away from the clamp, his yo-yo suddenly ran out. He stopped with a jerk but didn't lose his balance. He swore under his breath and looked around. He thought about unhooking. *Better*

38   T h e   B r i d g e   B u i l d e r s

not. He fiddled with straps and, like a magician, made the cord grow a few feet longer. Bolts tight, clamps off, steel connected, job done.

Danny did an about-face on the beam, stepping over the studs, and inched his way back to safety.

"There's the glory," he said, as the crane lifted the clamps into the sky.

●   ●   ●

Like soldiers, ironworkers tend to be a congenial group, at least among themselves. The inherent danger of their job creates bonds and separates them from other workers. Ironworkers will tell you straight up that they are special. *We're not bragging,* they'll say. *It's just the way things are.* Until they erect the steel, no one — not the electricians, the plumbers, the carpenters — can do their jobs.

They are the cowboys of the sky and, like cowboys, they'll tell you they are a vanishing breed, and that they lament the new safety regulations, and how the rules have made what they do less crazy, less special.

They'll talk about the ironworkers of old, many of whom were their fathers and grandfathers, and how they rode the metal balls hanging from the cranes to their skeletal offices in the sky. They'll smile as they talk about how the old ones drank more, how when the ironworkers came to town, the bordello business boomed, how they sometimes pummeled each other on girders eight inches wide. Safety? Nets were for circuses, yo-yos for kids.

Tradition is important to ironworkers. They no longer work with iron; the beams they connect are made out of steel. But they still call themselves ironworkers because that's what their fathers and grandfathers were. Besides, they couldn't call themselves steelworkers. Steelworkers work in factories, safe on the ground.

With all the emphasis companies put on safety now, ironworkers will make it sound as if they're becoming sissies. But that's just talk. They know that construction work is one of the riskiest jobs in America, and within the construction industry, erecting structural steel is the most dangerous trade. On average, an ironworker dies every ten days in the United States, usually from a fall. Every ironworker has stories of falling or of near-death experiences.

Chris Rainey was a foreman on the towers, and at thirty-eight, one of the most experienced ironworkers. He was from Kentucky and had long blond hair and a mustache, and the kind of boyish good looks you might find in a country music star. When he wasn't working, he spoke in a quiet voice, but when the job revved up, his demeanor changed. His voice grew louder and sharper, and anger flashed from his eyes.

Over the years, Chris had had his share of close calls. One time while working on a power plant, he was on a truss ninety feet off the ground when the bolts popped out and launched him six feet into the air. Somehow, he landed on a nearby truss about eight inches wide, sticking the landing like a gymnast.

Chris and the others knew that danger did strange things to the mind. Any ironworker worth his tool belt will admit he has frozen at one time or another. They'll say that sometimes, when you look up at a load in the sky, and the clouds are moving, something happens inside your brain, and you suddenly feel as if you're falling. They'll say you instinctively drop into a crouch, then look around, hoping no one saw.

The ironworkers looked different from other laborers on the bridge. They wore their hard hats backward so the bill didn't block their view of the load above. They wore work shoes with flat soles so they could feel the metal better. Their tool belts weighed twenty pounds or more, and when they walked, they walked with a sense of purpose. Their tools clinked, and they looked like GIs carrying ammunition. When it was warm, Chris and the others wore

denim work shirts with the sleeves cut off, which was more comfortable and showed off their biceps. Once, two women in a Camaro stopped on the old, adjacent bridge, whistled, and took pictures of them.

On the job, the ironworkers were as surefooted as mountain goats. Off the job, they got into all kinds of trouble. Chris Rainey had never been hurt badly hanging iron, but he had two steel rods and eight screws in his back from a car wreck. He broke both arms riding horses, broke his ribs playing football and broke his ankle working on a farm. Because they are risk takers by nature, many ironworkers are on their second or third marriages or have given up on the institution altogether, favoring "shacking up" instead. Like Spanish moss, their roots were planted in the air, and this made it hard on wives and children.

The best ironworkers lived like gypsies, traveling thousands of miles to a new city when the siren song of a big construction job began to play. Chris had spent the past thirteen years on the road, estimating that his total time at home added up to a year. Back home in Kentucky, his wife ran a dental office, and his two sons acted in movies sometimes and knew film star Tom Cruise. They used to cry when their dad left. Now, they simply asked, "When are you coming home?"

On weekends, ironworkers made their odometers work overtime. After quitting time on Fridays, Chris sometimes drove eight hours straight over the Blue Ridge Mountains to get home, arriving at two in the morning. On Sunday, just after bedtime, he hit the road again, reaching Charleston just in time to change for work. Those Mondays were tough, but coffee helped. Tuesday mornings were when he felt homicidal toward the alarm clock.

Because they were on the road, ironworkers took as much overtime as they could get; seventy hours a week was fine, and when the hours dropped to fifty-five or less, they got itchy and talked about "dragging up," finding

work elsewhere. A good ironworker might make $70,000 or $80,000 a year.

To save money, many ironworkers lived in campers. Chris found a spot in Fain's RV park near Interstate 26, underneath a main flight path for the Charleston International Airport. His camper was spacious and had a satellite dish, and some of his co-workers thought this made him a yuppie. A few feet away, Danny Fields lived in a tiny trailer he sometimes called his "shoebox." It had a table, a bed and a bathroom the size of an upturned coffin. Danny liked the trailer park, mainly because it was near a Waffle House.

● ● ●

Unlike Chris, Danny and the other ironworkers, Greg "Bink" Binkley wasn't an altitude junkie. He wasn't among the twenty-three percent of Americans who say they are "very afraid" of heights, but he did get butterflies. So, when Tom Mitcham, the general foreman on the west tower, asked him to walk onto a beam and bolt a panel, Bink thought, *I don't know about that.*

Technically, Bink wasn't an ironworker, at least from an ironworker's standpoint. "He's a welder," they would say, in a tone a high school senior might use describing a freshman. Ironworking was like any fraternity: It had a hierarchy, and you had to earn your way up. The top rung belonged to the connectors, guys who grabbed 47,000-pound steel beams dangling from the crane and muscled them into place. Then came less dangerous connecting jobs that ironworkers simply called "miscellaneous work." At the bottom were the poor souls sent to tighten bolts with ear-splitting impact wrenches. And, underneath the bottom rung were the welders and the rest of humanity.

So, as far as Mitcham was concerned, making Bink bolt the panel was a promotion. But as Bink stepped onto the beam's ten-inch ledge, he muttered, "I don't know about

OPPOSITE:
Chris Rainey, foreman,
Danny Fields (on radio)
and Leon Daman
(on edge girder)
connect floor beam.

this. I don't know about this." He tried to look straight ahead, but every once in a while, he saw the water 200 feet below, and adrenaline would shoot through him like an electric charge.

He bolted the panel tightly, though, and after that day, the butterflies in his stomach began to vanish. He had found his place on the bridge. He spent most of his time on the west tower, preferring it to the east because Dave Vannah was over there, and he thought Vannah was a loudmouth. He and Tom Mitcham's son, Slim, often worked together. One night, he and Slim were welding high on the towers, watching the sparks fall five, six, seven seconds and burst onto the rock islands, looking like upside down fireworks.

● ● ●

Tom Mitcham was the ironworker crew's general foreman. He hadn't put in as much time on iron as some of his crew, but he made up for it in life experience.

Tom was fifty years old, tall and lanky, and when he leaned against the metal railing on the edge of the bridge deck, he looked like a cowboy slouching on a ranch fence. He came from Texas and could trace his ancestors back to the early settlers of Austin. Unlike most ironworkers, he brought his family with him. He and his wife set up their camper in Goose Creek. His son, Slim, another ironworker, parked his camper a few yards away.

Like most ironworkers, Tom seemed hardwired to take risks. This enabled him to build steel towers, but sometimes left his personal life in tatters.

When he was eighteen, he joined the Navy and went to Vietnam, volunteering for a second tour on a gunboat. While in the service, he got married. When he returned from Vietnam, he learned that his new wife had passed $10,000 in bad checks. "I know it ain't fair, but you got to pay," a military officer told him.

He sold his beloved Shelby Cobra sports car to an oil executive to pay off the bad checks and started drag racing to pay his divorce bills. Like many people who thrive on adrenaline, he had a tendency to self-medicate. In his case, that meant drinking lots of beer. When someone brought over a twelve-pack, he downed all twelve and told them, "OK, where's yours?" He eventually found his way into construction and hanging steel, which suited his wandering spirit. He married again and divorced again, but remained hopeful. Like many things to him, marriage was like fishing: "You gotta keep throwing 'em back until you get a keeper."

He found a keeper in 1989. He had just finished a job on an ethylene plant in Texas and was drinking at a bar in his hometown of Wild Peach, fourteen miles from the Gulf of Mexico. The bar was having a New Year's Eve party in July, and he saw a woman over by the counter. His son, Slim, was nearby and will never forget the flash of his fa-

Tom Mitcham, general foreman, and his crew

Tom Mitcham, general foreman

ther's silver lighter moving toward the woman's cigarette. Tom married the woman, Patti, a pipefitter, who had been married three times herself.

One morning a few months into their marriage, Patti asked: "What's more important, drinking or your marriage?" He knew it wasn't a question. She was serving notice. And he didn't promise her anything, because that's what alcoholics do all the time. He just never had a drink again, finding strength in a twelve-step program prayer: *God, grant me the serenity to accept the things I cannot*

change; courage to change the things I can; and the wisdom to know the difference. Sober, he thought about becoming a substance abuse counselor, but that work didn't pay enough.

So, he and his wife hit the road, traveling from one iron-working job to another. One day in 2003 while working in a power plant in Missouri, he picked up the March issue of *Industrial Tradesman.* On page fifty-three was an ad soliciting workers for the new Cooper River bridge. The pay was so-so, but the job had a fringe benefit: It was in

South Carolina, and South Carolina was known for its cat-fish.

For Tom, fishing was therapy, and after he quit drinking, he spent hours and hours in his boat, often taking along his son, Slim.

Slim was like his father: tall, friendly, and talkative. Iron-working literally was in Slim's blood. On his right bicep, he had a tattoo that said "Born to Hang." That and a Con-federate flag tattoo had gotten him into trouble during a short stint in the Army. He spent three hours explaining to a sergeant how ironworkers have a special bond, and that he felt he was born to hang iron, not people.

Unlike his father, Slim had a temper. He quarreled with some of the other ironworkers. They thought he was too cocky; he thought they were just jealous. "I was reading blueprints when I was fourteen." He held a special con-tempt for the Europeans working on the cables. One day, he tossed a French worker's bike onto a metal shed, re-marking that "anything with wheels ought to have a mo-tor."

Slim had gotten into a few confrontations with the other workers, and his father had saved his job more than once, causing some to grumble about favoritism. But Tom was-n't blind. Of course, his son would make mistakes, on this job, in his life. Who doesn't? He was just glad his boy was with him, because is there anything more affirming and terrifying to a father than to see his son follow in his foot-steps?

ABOVE:

Slim Mitcham

LEFT:

Tom Mitcham

Benoit Monthean hangs cable

Chapter Seven

Culture Clash

Late 2004

I t was a festive night in downtown Charleston, with Christmas lights sparkling in store windows. A string of lights also twinkled on the staircase up to Bea Aaronson's art studio on King Street where Nico Blanchard stood, his hand warming a glass of red wine.

Hours before, Nico, a field engineer on the bridge, had showered and stripped off his work uniform: a pair of blue pants with red stripes on the leg pockets and a jacket with a patch that said "Freyssinet" on the chest. Now, he wore an orange short-sleeve shirt and blue jeans, a bold color scheme for December. But Nico made it work.

He had olive-colored skin, jet-black hair and piercing dark eyes. Women checked him out all night, but Nico's attention was on just one, his girlfriend, Sorane Rotellini, the artist. She had dark eyes and wore a low-cut lime green sweater. She was twenty-six, the same age as Nico, and grew up in a neighboring town in the French Pyrenees. Tonight, she was unveiling her paintings at the gallery, and Nico wanted everything just right.

His eyes darted about the room. He made sure the music never stopped and the wine bottles never emptied. Then a woman entered the gallery and was drawn to one of Sorane's nudes. Sorane asked the woman to write the $190 check in Nico's name. Nico smiled as he folded the check and put it in his pocket. The night was going well.

As more visitors poured in, so did Nico's buddies from the bridge, including his boss, Oliver Forget, project manager for Freyssinet International. Oliver hand-picked his crew for this project, finding workers from Brazil, Portugal, Canada, Mexico, Singapore, Germany, and a few from the United States. One American, David Schwandner, earned the nickname "birdman" twenty years ago after he leaped 125

Nico Blanchard, Etienne Delcroix, and Benoit Monthean at art show

feet off Tampa's Sunshine Skyway Bridge to avoid being hit by a falling crane. Oliver found them places to live in Charleston and had the company pay their rents. They were a rowdy, tight-knit group, and many took apartments and houses on Folly Beach, drinking hard at the Sand Dollar on weekends.

The Freyssinet crew was there to hang 128 cables on the bridge and strengthen concrete in the deck. In bridge-building circles, Freyssinet was well-known. In the early 1900s, Eugene Freyssinet found a way to make concrete stronger by "pre-stressing" it. This was done by placing steel cables in a slab and tightening the cables to compress the concrete. Installing bridge cables involved similar work, and Freyssinet would hang cables on many of the world's largest cable-stayed bridges. In recent years, crews had worked on the Millau Bridge in France, with towers taller than the Eiffel Tower, and the Rion-Antirion Bridge in Greece, built in time for the 2004 Olympics. They were used to working in foreign countries and dealing with the prejudices that go along with that. They faced these stereotypes soon after they arrived in Charleston.

"Frenchies," the Americans called them.

"Only one of them knows how to speak American."

"They don't work as hard as we do."

"Pretty boys."

Some American workers thought the Freyssinet workers were arrogant, or at the very least, stubborn. In Europe, safety glasses weren't always required. Not so in America, and Dave Vannah was forever yelling at the Freyssinet workers to put them on. They sometimes called him "Mr. Safety Glasses" in return. Communication was tough even under less excitable circumstances.

During a meeting with supervisors one morning, Oliver asked how crews would remove a set of counterweights on the deck. The weights rode on metal tracks and helped keep the towers straight and deck balanced.

"How are you going to dismantle the whales?" Oliver asked.

"Huh?" said Dennis Schumacher, an engineer from Ohio.

"Riles," said Roy Wilson, a Brit in charge of the iron-workers.

"Rails," said Tom Messervy, a field engineer from South Carolina.

José Lopes, a Freyssinet superintendent, had been with the company for twenty-six years and was used to this linguistic gumbo. He spoke Portuguese, Spanish, and French fluently, though his English was spotty. He was fifty-two years old and stocky, with a thick mustache and stern face. He had lost track of how many bridges he had worked on. In the past five years, he lived in apartments in Taiwan, Spain, Portugal, Greece, France, and, now, America. His three children grew up mostly without him, but he had made enough money to send his children to good schools and buy three homes in Europe he rarely lived in.

Over the years, he had learned to fend for himself with a certain amount of style. He stocked the fridge in his Folly Beach condo with French and Portuguese wines. He

cooked multi-course meals that he and his two Freyssinet housemates shared over several hours. He thought American restaurants rushed things too much.

He also had developed his own way of communicating with foreign crews, using hand gestures, whistles, and the universal phrase, "It's OK, it's OK." Instead of telling workers what to do, he showed them. In China, workers sat quietly like pupils waiting for his demonstrations. It was different on this project, though. The Americans asked a stream of questions until they understood, and they worked harder, quitting only for a half hour at noon for lunch.

Still, many Freyssinet workers thought American men wanted to be "masters of the universe," and they often cit-

Nico Blanchard feeds strands into pipe

Nico Blanchard

ed President Bush, whom they universally despised. They thought Americans as a group just wanted to consume, consume, consume, especially when it came to food. One morning when a receptionist brought in three boxes of doughnuts for a meeting, Oliver asked, "*Super Size Me.* Have you seen it?", referring to a documentary about a man who ate at McDonald's for a entire month and gained twenty-five pounds.

But many also found Americans unusually warm, and as time passed, they made connections to them and the place. Oliver and his fiancée decided to get married in Washington Square in downtown Charleston under the old live oaks, and he invited a dozen other Americans from the bridge. When his wife got pregnant, they decided the baby should be born in Charleston and be an American citizen.

The work itself was somewhat tedious, though. First, the Freyssinet crews welded pieces of white polyethylene pipe together. The pipe's purpose was to protect them from corrosion. A small groove spiraled around the pipe, which helped wick away rain in a heavy storm. Without the groove, rain could collect on the cables, weighing them down.

Once the pipe was ready, workers threaded a master strand through it and lifted them with a tower crane to an anchor on the tower. Workers on the road deck then fed more strands up the pipe, using a device that looked vaguely like an old-fashioned spinning wheel. Up inside the towers, other workers tightened the strands to the anchor with a hydraulic jack that looked like a giant screwdriver.

The longer the cable, the more strands the workers had to feed up the pipes, and as the last cables went up, workers were cramming more than ninety strands into each pipe. The longest cable was 807 feet long. Each strand in these cables was made of smaller steel rods that were twisted around each other, and those rods were manufactured by Georgetown Steel.

The plant was just sixty miles away, a dirty brown factory looming over Georgetown's old downtown. The mill had seen its share of financial problems over the years, and in October 2003, the mill's owners shut down the plant and filed for bankruptcy protection.

At first, Oliver wasn't particularly concerned. *This is America*, he thought. S*urely a superpower has other steel factories.*

But the more he and other managers searched, the more they learned about the limits of the United States steel industry. Most mills in the nation were making steel from recycled metals. Georgetown Steel was one of the few using raw materials, which enabled them to make stronger strands.

Oliver grew more and more nervous. According to his contract, Freyssinet had to buy from an American plant. If he wanted this requirement waived, he would have to seek approval from an array of state and federal agencies, and that could take months. Even if everyone signed off, finding an overseas supplier would be tough. A global construction boom had made it difficult for steel mills anywhere to supply steel rods on short notice. Oliver's deadline was May 2004, just a few months away. If he didn't find a supplier by then, his crews would run out of cable by October. Work on the towers would all but stop.

Oliver worked with people from Sumiden Wire Products of Tennessee, which had turned the rods from Georgetown Steel into strands. Sumiden managers visited several American steel plants. None could make the rods to the proper specifications.

Then Oliver heard someone mention North Star Steel in Texas. He immediately bought a plane ticket to Houston. They hadn't made these kinds of rods before, but Oliver urged them to try. "It would be good for your business to have your name attached to this bridge," he told them.

North Star's managers agreed, and they began making test rods in February. The first batches came back with too many defects.

They made more rods in March. Same problem.

On the third try, about sixty percent met South Carolina's standards. Better, but not great.

Oliver was getting desperate. Decision time. He placed an order for 1,300 metric tons of steel rods, 400 tons more than he needed. It was a huge waste under ordinary circumstances, but if he ordered that much, he would get enough rods to finish the bridge. The decision cost his company $300,000.

By late September, the first of the Texas rods arrived, and Oliver began to relax. Now his crews could focus on hanging the cables. Work began to settle into a rhythm, interrupted sometimes when Freyssinet workers fought with the ironworkers over who could use the tower crane. One afternoon, a Freyssinet crew drove past some American workers and splashed mud on them, a mortal sin on a construction site, and Oliver feared there would be a fight. Even after all these months on the bridge, most of the

Freyssinet workers on the road deck

Freyssinet workers still kept to themselves during the work day. But José and Dave Vannah eventually became friends, even though they didn't always understand each other's words. Dave respected José's work ethic, and José appreciated Dave's openness. "Ah, Big Dave," José would say and thump his heart with his fist. Both had trouble sleeping because they thought too much about the job at night.

One cold afternoon during the fall of 2004, José shouted and whistled at Jack Brady, an ironworker driving a forklift. Jack hit the brakes, and José pulled a piece of paper from his back pocket. Jack grabbed the paper without saying a word. Better to look at the numbers instead of trying to figure out what José was trying to say. The paper told him he had the wrong reel of steel, and he turned his forklift around. Dave asked what happened. "It's OK, it's OK," José said, waving his hand in the air, and that was enough for Dave. Dave slapped him on the back as they walked toward José's truck. They fell into a comfortable silence and leaned against the side of the truck, puffing on their cigarettes and gazing up at the towers.

Chapter Eight

East and West

Summer 2004

Pete Gibbs looked at his older brother, Everett, and Dave Vannah. "I've made a decision," Pete said.

Pete had supervised much of the towers' construction. But Wade Watson, the project manager, wanted him to focus on a section of the Charleston interchange to make sure it kept pace.

"Dave, you're going to run the east," Pete said. "And Everett, you're going to run the west."

Dave phoned Susan with the news: "I've got one of the towers!"

For Dave, this was a big promotion. Six years ago, he was the bottom rung on a ladder, lugging two-by-fours on a bridge in Bath, Maine.

Now, the east tower of North America's largest cable-stayed bridge was his. He felt a sense of freedom, almost as if he was running his own business. Some mornings, as he drove toward the towers, he saw the cables shining golden from the rising sun. It gave him chills.

Sometimes, like a new parent, he overcompensated. For a while, he had everyone do calisthenics in the morning after they trudged off the crew boat. That didn't go over well. Some workers couldn't touch their toes. Others thought it was just a weird idea. Construction workers? Exercise? What next, yoga? Mutiny was in the air, and Dave relented.

Over the months, though, Dave shaped the east tower crews in his own image. They were loud and brash, and they worked like an engine at full throttle.

"What the hell's going on? Are we having a tea party in here?" Dave bellowed after catching five of his crewmen together inside a trailer.

"I'm going to kick you off this bridge if I come back up here and you don't have your safety glasses on," he barked at another.

Then his Nextel would beep. Susan. "OK, sweetheart. I love you, too."

He tried to build morale. *A man needs a sense of pur-*

OPPOSITE:

Dave Vannah

Joe Rush, carpenter

pose, and if you can tap into that, he can do amazing things, he thought. "We're building the greatest bridge in the world!" he often shouted. One day, he bought everyone fried chicken, shelling out one hundred dollars from his own pocket. He forgave the occasional prank. One cold morning, he turned on his truck to get the heater going. When he stepped away, Carlos Ferguson, a carpenter, switched on the air conditioner, turning the truck into a refrigerator.

Dave saw the jokes as a sign that his crew was coming together. He wanted it to be like a big family, and when his son joined him on the site, it began to feel more and more like one. Scott was twenty-two, a slimmer version of Dave and with sharper facial features. Other workers teased him because he drank Slim-Fast and was the boss's son and younger than everyone else. They liked to make

him squirm by cracking jokes and imitating his father. He thought, *Should I join in, or ignore them?* He did a little of both.

Scott had worked with Dave in Myrtle Beach and spent four months on the new Cooper River bridge in 2003. But after Thanksgiving that year, he was fired when he failed to show up for work. Scott went back to Maine, but Dave told him: Work somewhere, get a good reference, and maybe you can get your job back. A year later, Scott reapplied and was assigned to his father's tower. Unlike his dad, Scott didn't think of bridge building as a calling. He did it because he enjoyed working with his hands, and because the money was good.

On the bridge, Dave told Scott that he was an employee with Palmetto Bridge Constructors, not his son. But Scott sometimes slipped up and called him Dad, and Dave often watched him out of the corner of his eye. One warm day when Scott was on the tower's concrete crossbeam, more than 200 feet above the river, Dave reminded him to tie off if he went near the edge. Later, Dave sent carpenter Joe Rush to work with Scott. "I'm asking you not because he's my son, but because I don't want anyone working on the crossbeam alone."

Dave and his crew sometimes stopped for a few moments to watch the workers on the west tower hang steel and pour concrete. And as the gap between the two towers narrowed, Dave tried to play up the idea that the two towers were in a race, even though the pace was really being set by Peo Halvarsson back in the offices off Morrison Drive.

"Look at what they're doing on the west," Dave told his crew.

Then he took a boat across the river to the west tower and told Everett's guys: "Look at what they're doing over on the east."

●   ●   ●

When Everett Gibbs took over on the west tower, the crew had been worn down. Workers had cuts and bruises and tired eyes. *These men have been worked too hard*, he thought. He knew that you can squeeze an orange for only so long before you run out of juice. So Everett stopped work for three days and had his crew do light cleanup work. He organized shifts so the hours would be more predictable. After that, work began to settle into a more bearable rhythm, and the deck began to grow quickly toward the east.

Everett and Dave Vannah were a study in contrasts. Where Dave was loud and wore his heart on his sleeve, Everett answered questions with a word or two. Unlike Dave, he rarely socialized with colleagues after hours, preferring to shoot pool at a biker bar in North Charleston.

Like Dave, Everett was attracted to risky occupations. Back home in North Carolina, he was a volunteer firefighter – "the only white man in an all-black department," he was fond of saying. For him, there was no greater high than rushing into a burning building. But seeing charred bodies and homes had given him a keen appreciation of danger. *Firefighters are always looking for things that can kill them*, he thought. Construction workers were less vigilant. *If they didn't have someone like me looking out for them, they would get hurt.* Just as the east tower reflected Dave's wide-open personality, the west was like Everett, a low and steady boil. Some workers on the west called the guys on the east "Yellos" because they seemed to "yell all the time," and vowed never to work on that side.

As autumn grew closer, Wade Watson and Peo Halvarsson thought that if they could combine Dave's enthusiasm with Everett's quiet no-nonsense style, they would have

Everett Gibbs, superintendent, west tower

per-hour winds before tearing apart. Their calculations also showed the bridge could handle winds as high as 110 miles per hour for shorter periods. But state officials weren't taking any chances. They required Palmetto Bridge Constructors take out $200 million in insurance coverage for any hurricane damage.

That August, Hurricane Charley was born in the Caribbean. Most hurricanes that hit Charleston begin as storms off the coast of Africa near the Cape Verde islands and curl through the Atlantic before spinning toward the United States. But Charley came in through the back door. It swirled through the Gulf of Mexico and sliced through western Florida, exiting near Jacksonville and spinning into the Atlantic. Then it turned like a boomerang back toward the Carolinas.

Just before dawn on Saturday, August 14, 2004, Charley's spiral arms began to brush the South Carolina coast. Soon, a dense band of rain hit Charleston Harbor. Winds blasted the bridge, creating an unusual aerodynamic effect on the approach ramp from Meeting Street. A 500-foot-long metal and plywood mold peeled back from the force.

But that was it. Winds on the ground were only fifty-four miles per hour, with gusts at the top of the towers reaching the high seventies. And, Charley was a speedy storm. It was gone by mid-morning, leaving behind a patchwork of cottony clouds and blue sky.

Charley was one of five tropical bullets bridge workers had to dodge. In six weeks, Bonnie, Frances, Ivan, and Jeanne would threaten the coast. Each time one approached, bridge crews quit what they were doing, tightened the hurricane straps and secured the cranes. It usually took a day or two to do all this, but they usually had plenty of warning. Then, during the last weekend of August, Tropical Storm Gaston formed suddenly off the Carolina coast, growing to hurricane strength as it spun toward Charleston.

ABOVE:
Joe Fisher and Scott Vannah spread rebar, east tower

RIGHT:
Peo Halvarsson

the perfect bridge crew. They also knew that this debate would be moot soon; the decks were moving quickly toward each other, section by section, cable by cable. Only a hurricane could stop them now.

●   ●   ●

In August 2004, the new bridge was as vulnerable as it would ever be. Until workers connected the decks, a medium-sized hurricane could push and pull on the decks and torque the towers. Engineers had tested a four-foot model of the bridge in a wind tunnel and found the towers could withstand an hour of steady seventy-five-mile-

Everett Gibbs, Dave Vannah and their crews reported to work at six in the morning that Sunday, thinking they would have most of the day to get ready. But by the time they arrived, the sky was an angry gray and wind-driven raindrops pelted their faces like thousands of flying needles. Dave and Everett told their crews to go home. Nothing to do now but ride it out.

No crew boats were running to the tower islands, so they jumped into Dave's truck and sped toward the Pearman bridge, hoping to keep an eye on everything from there. But a police officer stopped them. The bridge was closed, the officer said. They told him who they were, and he took down their names. After confirming that they worked for Palmetto Bridge Constructors, he let them on.

As they drove onto the Pearman, the winds grew stronger. Dave gripped the steering wheel to keep it steady. It was as if the wind had hands. A gust picked up the front end of the truck and slammed it down. Then another gust lifted the rear end and dropped it. Dave said he was getting scared, but Everett kept his poker face. It could be a lot worse, he told Dave. "Wait till a real hurricane rolls through."

Dave was especially worried about a large crane on the east tower that hadn't been secured. They drove back and forth on the Pearman, looking at their towers and that crane, unable to do anything but worry and wait. Once, Dave ventured out of his truck, but the wind grabbed the door from his grip and broke one of the hinges. Winds reached hurricane strength as the eye passed north of the city. After five hours, the winds died down, and Dave relaxed.

Even though they didn't have time to secure the bridge and their equipment, Gaston didn't cause any serious problems. Dave eventually replaced the hinge on the door of his truck, but it still creaked. Months later, whenever he climbed in and out, he would hear that noise and think of Hurricane Gaston and that anxious day.

Fernando Lara and Jack Brady,
ironworkers, east tower

61

Chapter Nine

The Gap Narrows

Late fall 2004

There's a saying on many work sites: "Construction is the only business where you work yourself out of a job." And at some point in a big job, anxiety sets in. Old timers call it "rambling fever."

Like many on the bridge, Terry Brown was thinking about his future in the autumn of 2004. By that time, the bridge decks were arching toward each other, and the towers and cables stood like two giant harps in the harbor. Terry had been on the bridge for more than two years, and before that had spent several years tying rebar and doing other construction jobs in the Southeast. But at thirty years old, he was tiring of the brutal hours and gypsy nature of construction. During lunch breaks and at night, he studied for an insurance license, sometimes talking with Joseph "Mr. Joe" Davis, who encouraged him to stay focused about his future.

But Terry also felt the bridge's pull, the need to see it through. Throughout those fall months, he kept asking himself, *Should I stay, or should I go.*

● ● ●

The end of a big bridge job is often a blur of meetings, last-minute problems and improvisation. It's a time when designers and engineers learn whether all the calculations they made over the past few years were correct. By now, crews knew what they were doing and did their work quickly, but the project often lurched to a halt, stalled by the last-minute tinkering of engineers, or when a large ship passed underneath and crews had to move the work barges.

During these breaks, workers had a few moments to lean on a temporary safety railing on the bridge deck and talk about the night a thunderstorm marched down the Wando River and threw a lightning bolt at the Grace bridge, causing everyone to scatter. Or when gusts blew workers' hardhats around like so much confetti. Or when

OPPOSITE:

Mark Sisney and Jack Brady, east tower

a chunk of metal fell from a crane onto a trailer, crashing through the sink in the trailer's john. Sometimes, they watched dolphins play below, or checked out sunbathing women on speedboats slicing through the waves. They marveled at the big yachts, and the people on them who seemed to have so much time on their hands. "They're probably not any happier than we are," Everett said one afternoon, his right cheek bulging with chewing tobacco. It was during those quiet moments that Everett thought about his four young children five hours away in North Carolina. His thoughts often fell like dominoes — how he hadn't seen his kids for weeks, how he was missing their childhoods, how you can never get those moments back. He scanned the horizon, because from so high on the deck, it felt like you could see everything, maybe back home if you looked hard enough.

Then, the job cranked up again, and daydreams vanished like a magician's handkerchief. Everett and Dave Vannah were back with their crews at full speed again, rushing to put the last pieces of this big puzzle in place.

November 1, 2004

A milestone: Workers connected the ramp from Charleston to the west tower. Chris Rainey grabbed a forty-seven-foot girder dangling from a crane, hooked up a come-along and cranked it seventy-eight times to winch the steel in place.

Now, Chris and the others could drive to the towers instead of climbing onto crew boats. For the engineers, this connection was a vindication of sorts. Designers had built in a six-inch margin in case the bridge didn't line up. But after more than three years and thousands of calculations, the girders were off by less than half an inch.

November 23, 2004

BOOM.

A steel cable inside the deck snapped, launching chunks of concrete 280 feet down the highway deck. Tom Messervy, the field engineer for the west tower, had just taken a measurement near the cable when it blew. The force lifted him in the air and tore the back of his pants off. Debris blasted his hardhat and cracked it. He landed on his feet somehow and staggered away.

Terry Brown was about twelve feet away and was hit. A piece of shrapnel shot toward his thigh, hitting a cell phone in his pants pocket. The phone was destroyed, but his leg was saved.

Everett Gibbs was fifteen feet away behind a compressor and was on the radio seconds later, in rescue mode. He had a funny feeling about that cable. He knew that Tom Messervy had been concerned about a weak point, and he knew that when crews tightened the cables, they would put 188,000 pounds of force on each one. So he had made sure everyone stayed back for ten minutes, just in case. *But this came out of nowhere*, he thought.

Tom and Terry weren't seriously hurt, but a near-death experience naturally makes you take stock. Tom had sailed through The Citadel, valedictorian of his class, and earned his master's at Massachusetts Institute of Technology. He had always had faith in God, and the snapped cable strengthened that bond. Later, when he walked past the spot where the cable snapped, he said a short prayer.

Terry Brown thought the accident was an omen, a sign that he shouldn't wait any longer to leave. He quit a few weeks later and began selling insurance.

December 15, 2004

The wind cut through the east tower like a scalpel as crews lowered concrete panels onto a bed of steel, connecting the east tower deck to the Mount Pleasant ramps. "We're not an island anymore," said Brian Clark, the field

Danny Fields, Chris Rainey, ironworkers

engineer for the east tower. Dave Vannah huddled with him in the cold. "We've shed a lot of blood, sweat, and tears to build this great bridge. In a few months, people will be driving over the bridge, and we'll all be gone."

January 6, 2005

One more hurdle before the connection: the bearings.

The bridge's 128 cables now supported the deck, but without the bearings, the deck could swing from side to side and damage the towers. The bearings would hold the deck in place but also allow it to move in an earthquake. Inserting the bearings would be like sticking a cork back in a wine bottle, except in this case, each cork weighed more than an SUV and the bottles were 573 feet tall. Workers had just a few inches of clearance to insert the bearings, and to get that clearance, crews would use more

ABOVE:
José Lopes after accident

OPPOSITE:
A C-17 cargo jet framed by
the cables

than a dozen hydraulic jacks to move the road deck sideways. Dennis Schumacher, chief engineer for the main span, had been working on the installation plans for months. He joined Dave Vannah, Everett Gibbs and the other supervisors in a conference room.

Dennis began: The deck would have to be jacked up a few inches and to the side four inches. Everything would have to be done exactly as he described.

Dave Vannah's Nextel beeped. He listened for a moment and then interrupted the meeting. "Excuse me, I gotta go, José got hurt pretty bad." Dave rushed out the door.

Dennis continued. Jacking the bridge would create enormous pressure, as much as four million pounds of force. "We're close to overstressing the concrete," he said. "We're very close to overstressing the edge girders." Too much stress, and the towers might be compromised.

Peo Halvarsson's Nextel went off. It was Dave. "How bad is it? Is he unconscious?"

Half an hour later, Dennis wrapped up his presentation, a touch exasperated, like a teacher who knows his students will need a review class. Dave Vannah returned, looked down at the table and rubbed his cheeks. José had been hit in the face by a winch, he told everyone. "He's got a messed up face. It might have taken his eye out. It broke his glasses and everything. It was probably my fault. I've been trying to inspect everything, but they have done this so many times - I guess I should have, I don't know."

But José was back on the bridge the next day. His eye was OK, though both were blackened with bruises. Twenty-one stitches stretched across the ridge of his nose. It would be another two weeks before he told his wife in France what happened.

January 2005

Bink had made it through several layoffs. But with just two months left before the connection, he made some welds that an inspector didn't like. Dave Vannah decided that Bink had to go, and on Friday, pay day, Tom Mitcham pulled Bink aside and said this was his last check. "We're gonna lay you off."

Bink was stunned. He had hoped to stay through the connection, at least. The job had been important to him. He had photos of the bridge at home; he had taken his teen-age daughters up one weekend to show off his work. *Pretty cold way to end*, he thought. A few weeks later, he found a job installing modems and telephones.

Chris Rainey took off for a job in Ohio, just two hours from his home in Kentucky. A few days later, Danny Fields left as well. The bridge wasn't the same without his pal, Chris, and the work was winding down anyway. He phoned a project manager for a new power plant going up near Charlotte.

"Danny, are you still on that bridge?" The project manager hired him on the spot.

Danny woke up before dawn the next morning, a Saturday. It was dark and about thirty-seven degrees. He wiped his face with a white cloth and started packing. Another ironworker, Joe Hill, called him on his cell phone to make sure he was up. Danny wanted to be on the road in time to make a birthday party for his seven-year-old daughter.

He backed his blue Chevy pickup toward the camper but had trouble connecting it to the hitch. He had to stop for a few moments to warm his hands. A few minutes later, as the sun began to rise, he pulled his trailer out of Fain's RV Park for good, passed the Waffle House where he ate most of his meals, and made his way to North Carolina and his daughter. But he was home for only a day and a half. By Monday, he was gone again, on his way to hang iron in Charlotte.

As the connection grew near, Tidewater Skanska transferred Everett Gibbs to a road project an hour and half from his home in North Carolina. He looked relieved, smiling more than he did a few weeks before.

With Everett gone, Dave had both towers, and with so many people leaving, he suddenly found he had a manpower deficit. When Terry Brown called Dave one day to sell him life insurance, Dave sold him on coming back to the bridge.

"You were one of the original guys on the towers," he said. "It's only for a few weeks. Why come so far and not see the bridge completed?"

Terry thought about it over the weekend and called Dave on Monday. He was coming back.

March 2, 2005

A week before the connection, Victoria Lucas clutched two pictures of her son Miguel, the only worker to die on the bridge. Victoria's teary eyes focused on the smiling face beneath the glass frames as she remembered the last time she spoke with him.

It was five in the morning, May 10, 2004, the day before his death. He lived next door, and he called to check on her before he left for work. "Miguel was so kind, so happy," she said out loud, to the pictures in the frames. Having him nearby made it easy for her to take care of him. She made him lunch every day. He liked her sandwiches and hamburgers the best. She knew the last lunch she made for him was never touched.

Her eyes brightened as she remembered the cups of coffee they shared. He bought a good, flavored coffee from a cafe downtown. He would hold out the cup for her to take a sip and then kiss the top of her head, saying, "Hola Máma" and "Eres mi diosa." Oh Mamma. You are my goddess.

Her hands trembled when she remembered the phone call from the priest. She was cleaning rooms at the Embassy Suites when it came. The priest said, "One of your sons has fallen from the bridge."

"Which one? I have three up there."

The priest didn't tell her. She hurried home, where her oldest daughter asked her to sit, and then softly said: "Mamma, it was Miguel."

She blamed herself for bringing the family to America. She forbade her youngest son to return to the bridge. Despite her pleas, her oldest son continued to work for two more weeks. Then he quit, too. Miguel's brother-in-law stayed until the interchange job was done.

She stayed away from the bridge for months after her son's death. On the day after Halloween, Día de los Muertos, the Day of the Dead, she gathered a bouquet of roses and chrysanthemums to take to the spot where he fell, a custom in Mexico of honoring the dead. A supervisor stopped her and her family before they could set the flowers down.

As she held the pictures of her son, she vowed to visit the place where he died on every Day of the Dead as long as she lived near the bridge. If she can't leave flowers there, she will leave a bouquet for him on a peaceful spot along the Cooper River.

Chapter Ten

The Connection

n some European cultures, it's bad luck to be the first person to cross a new bridge. But for an ironworker, bragging rights will trump superstition every time. In late February 2005, with the girders on the east deck just three feet or so from the west, Philip Cotter knew what to do.

Philip was an ironworker from Tennessee, and his foreman, Jack Brady, had sent him to work on the beams. Philip saw the gap between them and yelled to Slim Mitcham on a barge 200 feet below:

"Hey, look up! You're about to see history!"

Philip then hopped from one girder to the other and did a little strut.

"You looked like a flying squirrel," Slim said afterward.

The workers would debate whether Philip's leap counted as a crossing, but as far as Jack Brady and the other experienced ironworkers were concerned, Philip was the first. "No matter what anyone tells you," Jack said later, "All the rest will be second or losers."

Philip's leap didn't make headlines that day, but the workers knew Friday would be different.

That day, they would lower the last concrete slab in place. Once that slab was in, the bridge deck would be all but done. Workers still needed three more months to clean up, install a pedestrian fence, and finish the ramps. But Friday, March 11, 2005, would be a birthday of sorts, the day the bridge truly linked one place to another. A ceremony would be held, and, as usual, crews were working overtime to get everything ready.

First, they had to bolt the decks together. To line them up, workers tightened some of the cables, taking into account a sudden temperature drop that had moved the deck a few inches. Once the deck girders were aligned, Jack Brady and his crew inserted 2,250 bolts. Jack tightened them himself with an impact wrench that made his body shake.

The crew finished bolting Wednesday afternoon. With the bones of the bridge connected, Peo Halvarsson ordered twenty-five pizzas. About forty workers gathered at the center of the span. Peo jumped on two concrete slabs,

OPPOSITE:

Jack Brady and Dave Vannah

adding another four feet to his six-foot-four frame. He told them he would hire any one of them on any bridge job in the future.

The next day, the workers began lowering the final ten slabs, and Dave Vannah was revving in the red zone.

"Hey, Simon, we're waiting for you! I'm glad the governor ain't here today!"

Simon Castaneda, a laborer from Ladson, moved quickly, climbing onto a girder. He balanced on the four-inch ledge, his heels hanging into the air.

"C'mon Simon! What are you waiting for!"

Simon glued a strip of foam to the girder that would hold the slab in place. Nearby, Jack Brady wrestled with the clamps.

"Jack! Jack! You're killing me!"

The first slab went in a few minutes later.

"It doesn't get much better than this!" Dave howled. "Bring it down, unhook it! Hook the other one up. Hallelujah!"

By that afternoon, nine slabs were in, and Dave raced across the deck, with José Lopes close behind. "Hallelujah!"

Only one piece of the puzzle was missing: The tenth slab would be left for the next day's festivities, the driving of the Golden Spike.

As the sun set, most of the workers were gone, and the bridge was quiet except for the wind. Peo went up to Roy Wilson, the man in charge of the ironworkers.

"Congratulations, Roy," he said, and shook his hand. Down below, rush-hour traffic on the Pearman bridge crawled toward Mount Pleasant, and the sun turned everything orange.

●   ●   ●

Friday, the big day.

Dave's eyes darted from one worker to another. He checked his watch every few minutes. He fiddled with his cigarette box. He wanted everything just right today, and he wanted his wife, Susan, with him when they dropped that final slab. *Where is she?*

She had a history of getting lost. One time, when she tried to find a new onramp from Meeting Street, she ended up on the way to Columbia.

At eleven, Susan called him from a pay phone at a gas station in Mount Pleasant. He gave her directions, shaking his head, and then rushed off in his truck to the offices on Meeting Street to get her a hard hat and safety glasses.

When he got back, he bumped into Tom Mitcham. Tom was leaving right after the ceremony, heading with his son, Slim, to hang iron in Texas at a fuel plant. Dave told Tom he wished he could stay longer. But Tom was ready to leave. "You gotta know when to go."

As noon approached, a convoy of cars, vans, and a tour bus drove up. The visitors spilled out, smiling, clutching their hard hats when they looked up, and shivering in the cold winds.

Many of the workers stood back. Tim "Chivo" Boswell, a carpenter from Oklahoma, and Mark Sisney yelled, "Get your peanuts! Get your popcorn!" Other workers soaked it in.

Joseph "Mr. Joe" Davis grinned from ear to ear. He had worked so hard on this bridge, made so many friends, helped build something that few people ever get to build: a landmark. *This was one of the happiest days of my life*, he thought. *I'm part of history today.*

Terry Brown was surprised how moved he felt by the moment. *All those long hours are paying off*, he thought and began to recall what these two tall towers looked like when they were half-built.

April Carder was a hundred yards or so away from the hubbub, dismantling an elevator. She didn't feel like celebrating, though. She knew she would be saying goodbye to the guys soon, and she was unsure about her future.

Simon Castaneda, laborer

At three minutes to noon, Dave looked down the bridge, hoping to see Susan, or his son, Scott, who drove down the approach ramp to look for her. Off in the distance, some people were walking toward them. *No, that's not them. No way she's going to make it now.*

The crowd gathered around the gap.

Two carpenters, Carlos Ferguson and Joe Fisher, and two ironworkers, Philip Cotter and Lewis Williamson, would set the final slab. "I'm not nervous," Philip said, knowing workers had set the slab earlier that day to make sure it fit.

Dave stood inside the red tape with Peo behind him.

Now, the dignitaries outnumbered the workers. In a tweed jacket, Arthur Ravenel Jr. watched with a grin. "Unbelievable," he said. "How those guys can walk out there, I just don't know." Ravenel, the bridge's namesake, was afraid of heights.

"Roll," Dave yelled.

The crane lifted the slab.

Philip twirled his hand, motioning to the crane operator to keep it coming.

"Looking good!" Dave said.

And then it went in, a perfect fit.

Main span workers

SERIES:

The west tower

from start to finish

Afterword

Three days after the connection, with the politicians and news people back in their offices, Dave Vannah rounded up sixteen of his workers and told them to get in their cars and trucks. They formed a convoy and drove from one end of the bridge to the other. Dave wanted his guys to be the first to drive over the bridge.

In the spring of 2005, the bridge was all but done. Palmetto Bridge Constructors had beaten its five-year deadline by more than a year. As workers cleaned up the deck and finished installing the lights for the cables, the bridge began its sometimes bumpy transformation from job site to public space.

One night after the connection, a seventy-one-year-old man named Bernie Ditter walked onto the bridge fully expecting to be stopped by a guard or some workers. But the site was empty, and as he jogged across, he felt like he was walking into a fantasy. *Everything seems so huge*, he thought. It was windy, and gusts strummed the cables. *It's like a giant harp.* When he made it to the middle, he looked down at the old bridges. *It feels like I'm floating.* He jogged the entire length. The next Sunday morning, he bragged to his friends at church: "I'm the first one to run over the bridge." Bernie Ditter's exploits infuriated Wade Watson and other managers with Palmetto Bridge Constructors. They said the bridge didn't officially belong to the state yet, and that Bernie had trespassed. But Watson's complaint had the ring of a parent scolding a teenager for violating a midnight curfew. The bridge was coming into its own.

Soon, charities were holding dinners on the bridge to raise money. On one private tour, a car salesman named Will Angelich proposed to Danielle Matcovich, a young software company manager. In April, a record 30,000 people signed up for the annual ten-kilometer Cooper River Bridge Run, the last one over the old bridges. As the runners flooded the Pearman, two people stood at the center of the new bridge: Big Dave Vannah and Tom Messervy, the tall field engineer who nearly lost his life when a steel cable exploded in the road deck. To the runners below, they looked like giants.

In mid-July, the bridge was ready for its debut. On July 9 and 10, community leaders opened the bridge for pedestrians, and 175,000 people showed up - 135,000 more than expected. Dave Vannah and his wife, Susan, were among the first in line. "It's pretty awesome to be here and be part of it," Susan said. Without his grubby work shirt on, Dave blended in with the crowd. But Peo Halvarsson, the tall Swede, stood out. He wore his boots and hard hat and people stared and congratulated him. His normally stern and formal demeanor was gone, replaced with an easy grin.

Many workers who had left the area for other jobs felt an irresistible urge to return. Chris Rainey, the ironworker, drove down from Kentucky with his wife, two sons, mother and sister. They all walked around in a daze on the giant steel and concrete stage Chris and the others had built.

ABOVE:
Susan and Dave Vannah
OPPOSITE:
Charleston in fog as viewed
from the east tower crane

81

"I can't believe there are so many people here," he said over and over. As he and his family strolled under the towers, a few people learned he was a bridge builder and began asking for his autograph. A mob grew around him. It started raining, but Chris kept on signing his name, the ink smudging sometimes. His two sons, who rarely see him as he travels from job to job, just smiled. Dad, the celebrity.

For the first time, anyone in Charleston could see what Chris and the other bridge builders saw every day. *The view is so different up here*, people said. Off in the distance, the Morris Island Lighthouse looked like a stick in a giant puddle. North of Mount Pleasant, toward the Cape Romain Wildlife Refuge, the land looked like a flat, green quilt. As Mr. Joe put it, everything looked so beautiful once you were above it.

●　　●　　●

Four days later, technicians set off 20,000 pounds of fireworks, the largest display in the state's history. As the smoke drifted through the harbor, Ruby Williams, winner of *The Post and Courier's* contest to light the bridge, pressed a button, and 37,000 watts coursed through the bridge's electrical system, slowly illuminating the towers and cables.

On July 16, 2005, the politicians gathered on the bridge to open it for traffic. The morning sun was white hot as speaker after speaker took the podium. They talked about symbols and progress and how the project was done

OPPOSITE: Open house

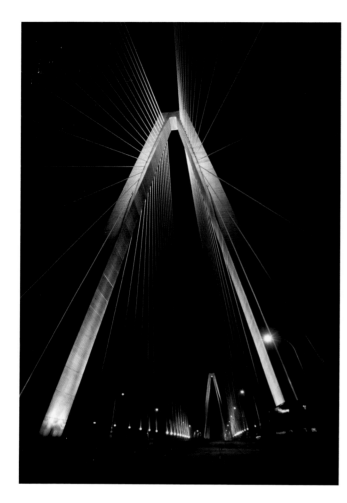

ABOVE: Illuminated for the first time

OPPOSITE: Ribbon cutting

ahead of schedule and without cost overruns. During the speeches, the bridge's designer, Mike Abrahams, stood in the shade of one of the bridge's 128 cables, gleaming white in the sun, and ran his hand along a large anchor block above his head. Finally, at 11:06 a.m., nineteen politicians sliced the red ribbon.

● ● ●

The day after the bridge opened, Dave and Susan Vannah packed their car. It was 9 p.m., and they had a nine-hour drive ahead of them. Dave had another bridge job, this one in Pensacola, Florida, a new bridge on Interstate 10 that had been wiped out by a hurricane. They had an early morning appointment with a realtor to look at a house.

They pulled onto Interstate 26 and saw the bridge glowing in the distance. It was a small detour, but Dave had to drive across one more time. Soon, he was rolling underneath the cables, and he remembered his buddy from France, Jose, and how they had shared smokes under the towers' shadows. He wished Jose could be there with him

now to see the cables lighting the night sky. He remembered how the bridge looked without its smooth concrete median, how storage sheds and tools were scattered everywhere. He remembered his crew, people like April, Mr. Joe, and Mark, hunkering inside to escape the sun, the rain, and sometimes him. Everything felt so different now, so tidy, foreign. He looked at Susan. "I'm going to miss this bridge. It's the greatest bridge in the world."

● ● ●

In a few months, Dave Vannah, Mr. Joe, April, and the others were gone from their bridge.

After installing more than 560 miles of cable strands, the cable crews headed back to France and Portugal.

After generating almost 13,000 drawings and documents, the engineers and managers flew back to Sweden and Britain.

After thousands of cups of coffee, thousands of hours of overtime and thousands of arguments and jokes, the rodbusters, carpenters, and ironworkers got jobs at other construction sites, or found something entirely different to do.

Today, they may even drive over the new bridge to their new jobs. Other motorists who might glance at them but have no idea that they're next to the guy who tied that rebar, the laborer who poured that concrete, or the ironworker who hung the steel. The bridge wasn't theirs anymore. It belonged to everyone, as it should. But for as long as they live, and as long as the new bridge stands, the workers will know what they made.

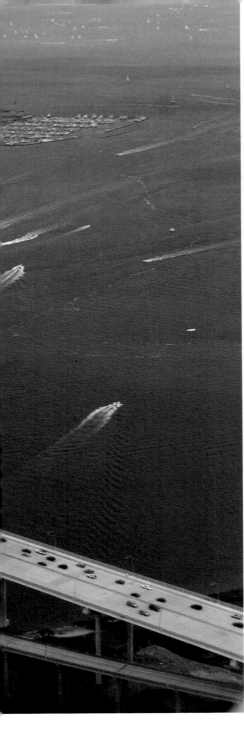

ABOVE: Farewell note on the
Grace bridge
OPPOSITE: Open for traffic

Acknowledgements

A bridge is a giant puzzle, and on a much smaller scale, so is assembling a book. Many people helped us with this puzzle. Above all, we're grateful for our time with the workers, who put up with our questions and let us into their lives. It was a privilege getting to know them. Bobby Clair Jr., project director for the state Department of Transportation, has a rare combination of engineering and political skills and instantly recognized the importance of giving the public a picture-window view of the bridge's progress. A very special thanks to Charles Dwyer, David Wertz, David Kinard, and all of the other engineers from the state who escorted us to the site and educated us about the bridge. Wertz was especially kind with his time. We're also grateful to Wade Watson, project manager for Palmetto Bridge Constructors, who was willing to let us watch the construction process unfold without trying to hide the inevitable ups and downs of any large project. Thanks also to Lars Landen, Peo Halvarsson, Roy Wilson, Dennis Schumacher, Everett Gibbs, Dave Vannah and the other managers. Their competence and patience were impressive.

An important source of inspiration and history for this book was Gay Talese, author of *The Bridge*. Written forty years ago, and recently re-published, this wonderful book documented the construction of New York's Verrazzano-Narrows Bridge. Talese's observations about building a "stage in the sky" and how workers catch "ramblin' fever" still apply.

We also are grateful for the support of *The Post and Courier*. Over the years, the newspaper went through vats of ink writing about the old bridges' problems, and without the guidance of Larry Tarleton, executive editor in the 1990s and now publisher, and Ivan V. Anderson, Jr., president of Evening Post Publishing Co., it's unclear whether the new bridge would be standing right now. Thanks also to Bill Hawkins, executive editor, and Steve Mullins, managing editor, for making this book happen. Doug Pardue, special projects editor, helped coordinate the reporting and design of our work and was masterful at keeping the project on track. Steve Knickmeyer, Angie Blackburn and many others at the paper also provided important feedback. Arlie Porter also deserves special recognition for his aggressive coverage of bridge-related issues over the years. Finally, we would like to thank those in our families, especially Hanson and Lola Abu, Luke Bartelme, Patricia, Maria and William Guerry, Mary, Benson, Tasha and Star James.

—Tony Bartelme, Jessica VanEgeren, August 2005

OPPOSITE:

One bolt at a time

Bridge facts

Total Length : 3.5 miles (including approaches)

Length of main span: 1,546 feet

Ship clearance at mid-span: 186

Width of main span: 141 feet, 10 inches

Height of towers: 573.5 feet

Tons of stone for tower bases: 1.6 million

Number of cables: 128

Longest cable: 807 feet

Concrete in bridge: 320,000 cubic yards

Traffic lanes: 8, plus a lane for bicycles and pedestrians.

Approach ramps: 15

Cost: $632 million

Construction began: July, 2001

Open for traffic: July 16, 2005

View from
Sullivan's Island

Photography credits

Yalonda James was a photographer for *The Post and Courier* and is now with *The Charlotte Observer.* Front and back covers, pages *vii*, 2, 11, 13, 14, 18, 19, 24, 27, 32, 36, 38, 40, 42, 44, 46, 48, 49, 50, 52, 53, 54, 56, 57, 58, 59, 60, 62, 64, 65, 66, 72, 76, 77, 80, 90.

Leroy Burnell is a photographer and assistant with *The Post and Courier.* Pages *xii*, 9, 30, 70, 78, 79, 88.

Mic Smith is a photographer for *The Post and Courier.* Pages *xi*, 3, 6, 17, 35, 43, 45, 51, 67, 75, 81, 84, 87, 92.

Wade Spees is a photographer for *The Post and Courier.* Pages *vi*, 4, 8, 12, 16, 20, 25, 89.

Alan Hawes is a photographer for *The Post and Courier.* Pages 21, 22, 28, 69, 82, 86.

Brad Nettles is a photographer for *The Post and Courier.* Page *34.*

Sam Roberts was an intern for *The Post and Courier.* Page *33*

About the cover: *Yalonda James photographed the bridge one foggy morning while in a manbasket dangling from the tower crane next to the east tower.*

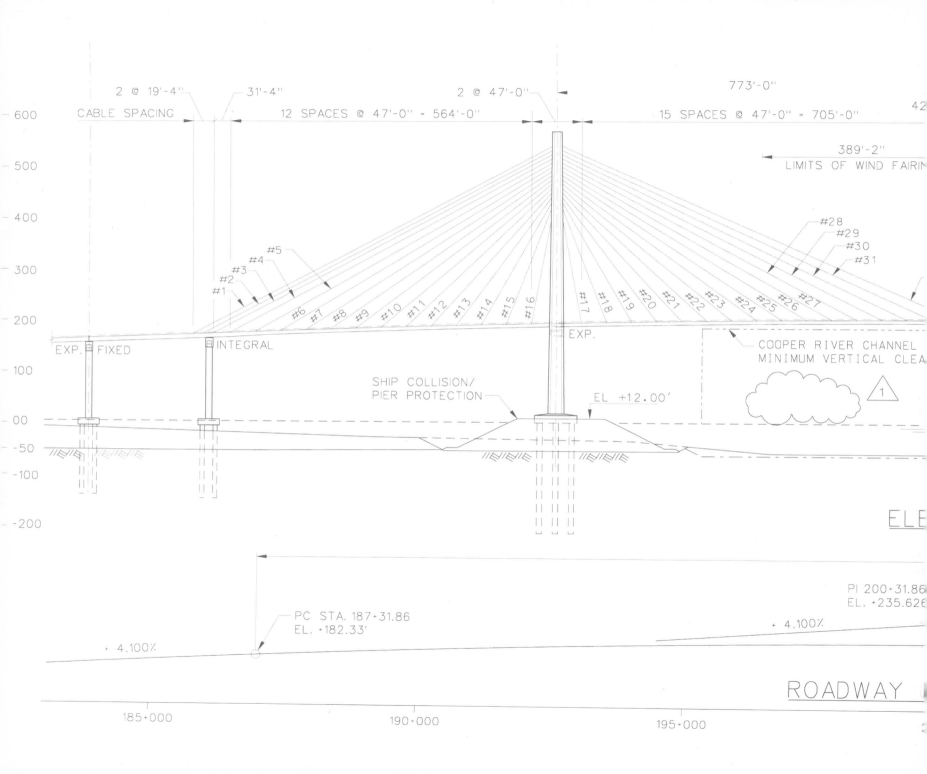

ELE

ROADWAY